the Forth
Naturalist
*and*Historian

KU-366-747

Volume 20

Published by the Forth Naturalist and Historian, University of Stirling – an approved charity and member of the Scottish Publishers Association. 1997.

ISSN 0309-7560

ISBN 1-898008-17-5

Supported by BP in Scotland.

Cover: front– Wallace: linocut by Stirling artist Owain Kirby
       back– The Old Burgh Seal of Stirling
Both by courtesy of The Smith Art Gallery and Museum, Stirling.

Printed by Meigle Printers Ltd., Tweedbank Industrial Estate, Galashiels.
Set in Zapf Calligraphic on 90gsm Fyneprint and cover white Astralux.

OLD LIMESTONE WORKINGS IN GLEN TYE
AND THEIR ASSOCIATED FLORA

John Mitchell

Glen Tye, which lies on the old county boundary between Perthshire and Clackmannanshire at the western end of the Ochils, holds several features of interest for the local historian, not least the tell-tale signs of limestone quarrying in the past. The present paper gives a brief sketch of the area's underlying geology, history of the former limestone workings and current agricultural use, followed by a description of the site both as a habitat and refuge for a number of locally uncommon plants.

The limestone workings, past and present

The British Geological Survey sheet for the district – *Alloa 39 East* (solid) – shows Glen Tye (NN 833020) to comprise mainly of sandstones and basalt lavas of Lower Old Red Sandstone age, collectively known as the Sheriffmuir Formation. The more detailed original geological field slips for the Glen Tye area record that the formation also includes mudstones with calcareous nodules. These are best described as 'concretionary limestones' and are almost certainly what were once quarried and burned for lime (I. H. S. Hall *pers. comm.*).

In common with all domestic (*ie.* non-industrial) winning of lime, there is no trade documentation available for the Glen Tye quarry; and unlike other known limestone workings around Stirling (see Mackay, 1977; Harrison, 1993), no mention of the activity is made in any relevant parish statistical account or county agricultural report. Nothing is shown on even the earliest ordnance survey map. This would seem to indicate that the Glen Tye workings had been abandoned before the end of the 18th century. Fortunately, some eye-witness statements on the practice can be gleaned from the evidence given following a summons raised by the Commissioners for the Annexed Estates in 1764 for the division of the Sheriffmuir commonty, of which lower Glen Tye formed its eastern edge. The unpublished case report (Scottish Record Office, 1772) reveals that limestone quarrying had been carried out alongside the Auld Wharry Burn and the Spout of Rivers Burn in Glen Tye since at least the 1680s. An accompanying plan of the commonty (SRO 1766) shows the workings as 'White Muck Holes', with two limestone burning kilns nearby. Although not made clear in the evidence, the lime extracted being of poor quality would have been used almost exclusively as an agricultural fertiliser.

Today, the old workings are most obvious on the north (Perthshire) side of the Auld Wharry Burn (Figure 1) and to the east of its main northern tributary, the Spout of Rivers Burn, at an approximate altitude of 260-310 m. The immediate area is fairly intensively grazed by hill sheep, as it undoubtedly has been for the last two hundred or more years.

Figure 1. Old limestone workings in Glen Tye at the confluence of the Auld Wharry
and Spout of Rivers Burns (NN 833020).

The limestone workings: botanical interest

The raised limestone spoil heaps and water-logged hollows between them
offer niches both for plants which thrive on a well drained soil and those more
suited to permanent dampness. No rare species have been recorded to date,
the site's botanical interest being the diversity of its calcicole (lime-loving) flora
compared with the acidic plant communities covering most of the Ochil range.
The selected list below is made-up of locally uncommon species that are
probably representative of the herb-rich grasslands which have long since
disappeared from the Sheriffmuir area due to land drainage together with the
introduction of cultivated grasses and artificial fertilisers:

Pink Stonecrop *Sedum villosum*, Grass-of-Parnassus *Parnassia palustris*, Fen
Bedstraw *Galium uliginosum*, Few-flowered Spike-rush *Eleocharis quiqueflora*,
Dioecious Sedge *Carex dioica*, Tawny Sedge *C. hostiana*, Long-stalked Yellow
Sedge *C. viridula* subsp. *brachyrryncha*, Quaking Grass *Briza media*, Early Marsh
Orchid *Dactylorhiza incarnata* subsp. *incarnata*, Northern Marsh Orchid
D. purpurella.

Also present is a fine colony of the Greater Tussock Sedge *C. paniculata*, a
species more typical of lowland wet woodland or the fringe vegetation of
standing water than the open hillside.

Although the botanical survey of the Glen Tye workings was undertaken
back in 1986, the above assemblage of plants – all with restricted distributions
in the western Ochils – would seem worthy of placing on permanent record.

Acknowledgements

I am grateful to Murray Dickie for first drawing my attention to the Glen Tye limestone workings and to John Harrison for generously making available his notes on the division of the Sheriffmuir commonty. Thanks are also due to Ian Hall of the British Geological Survey for comments on the original geological field slips covering the area; and to Allan Stirling for reading through the first draft of this paper.

References

Harrison, J.G. (1993). Lime supply in the Stirling Area from the 14th to the 18th centuries. *Forth Naturalist and Historian* 16, 83-89.

Mackay, K.J.H. (1977). Limestone working: a forgotten Stirlingshire industry. *Forth Naturalist and Historian* 2, 81-105.

Scottish Record Office (1766). *A Plan of Sheriffmuir* (RHP 1042).

Scottish Record Office (1772). *Division of the Commonty of Sheriffmuir* (CS 22/586).

BOOK REVIEWS (Naturalist)

Loch Lomond – a 2½ inch to the mile map, Milngavie to Ardlui. Ordnance Survey Outdoor Leisure No. 39. £5.40.

With No. 38, Ben Nevis and Glen Coe, the 93 mile West Highland Way is covered in detail by this large, double-sided, full colour map. An awkward handfull for 'on the road' study!

Images of Loch Lomond. Photographs by Willie Simpson, text by Alison Brown. Stirling History Services. 30pp. ISBN 1-870542-36-3. £1.95

Principally a well and colourfully produced visual memento for visitors, enhancing memories, but also showing from the photographer's extensive collection, dramatic landscapes and other pictures in weather conditions the summer visitor would never see.

L.C.

BOOK REVIEW (Naturalist)

Owls. Keith Graham, Colin Baxter Photography. ISBN 1-900455-23-4. 48pp. £8.

This booklet could be described as an attractively-produced, easy-to-read introduction to these remarkable birds of the night. It is the latest in a series of large, square-format books produced in association with the Scottish Wildlife Trust and is suitable for all people with a potential interest in nature aged eight and over.

Although the text is relatively concise, the author's enthusiasm for historical information, local names and the odd anecdotal reference to such acquaintances as 'Muhammed Owly' make the book more interesting. Useful summaries are given for each of the six British species on such general information as habitat preference, food and breeding behaviour, whilst some conservation issues are briefly mentioned in the main text. A small omission is the lack of any mention of the absence of the commonest species (the Tawny Owl) in Ireland.

The book is clearly printed and it is beautifully illustrated by a series of full-page photographs from some of the country's best known nature photographers – a potential present for younger readers in particular.

Bill Brackenridge

THE WEATHER OF 1996

S. J. Harrison

Recent trends towards a globally warmed climate, with warm westerly winds and heavy winter rains, seemed to have been set aside during 1996, which saw the return of winds from a more traditional easterly direction during the winter half-year. After the frost damage of Hogmanay 1995, low temperatures and snow were frequent. Spring was very late, with frosts well into May, and after a very mild autumn, cold easterlies and snow returned again in November. Although nowhere near as warm as 1995, summer temperatures frequently topped 20°C, and the June to September rainfall total was only 63% of the long-term average, culminating in a three-week dry spell between the 2nd and 22nd of September. At the end of the year the total rainfall was 92% of average.

Temperature and rainfall values in the following refer to Parkhead II climatological station unless otherwise stated.

January Cold and exceptionally dull

Daytime temperatures were low for the first six days but the cloud cover prevented night frosts. The cold and dull weather broke on the 7th over three wet and windy days during which the total rainfall was 17.3 mm. There was brief lull late on the 10th when the wind fell away and the sky cleared, resulting in patches of black ice by the morning of the 11th. Mild and unsettled weather continued, however, until the 14th and by the 15th the wind was a light southerly which kept daytime temperatures above 9°C. Easterly winds then held sway for the remainder of the month and by the 26th and 27th the daytime temperature struggled to reach 1.3°C in Bridge of Allan (–0.5°C Dunblane). Snow began falling late on the 26th and continued for most of the 27th. This accumulated to a depth of 5 cm in parts of the Forth Valley but exceeded 30 cm in Dunblane. Many roads, particularly over higher ground, became impassable. A slow thaw set in on the 28th but by the end of the month the snowline was still at 100 m. For much of Britain this was the dullest January on record and in parts of eastern Scotland the recorded hours of bright sunshine were less than 25% of average.

February Cold but quite sunny

There was bright sunny weather over the first three days, but night temperatures fell below freezing, reaching –5.6°C (–6.9°C Bridge of Allan). Heavy snow was falling by the morning of the 5th, which continued into the

6th. Parkhead recorded 19 cm (Dunblane 22 cm), while parts of Dumfries and Galloway registered in excess of 50 cm and the A(M)74 was closed, stranding many motorists for 24 hours. After a brief respite on the 7th, more snow began to fall on the 8th, but by the 9th this had turned to rain. The resulting snowmelt floods caused extensive disruption. Daytime maximum temperatures rose from –0.1°C on the 6th to 7.5°C on the 10th. The weather remained mild, wet and windy until the 13th when night frosts returned. On the 17th a northerly airstream became established and the weather was bitterly cold, with snow flurries, until the 22nd. There were spells of rain between the 23rd and 25th, which eventually turned to snow. There was a light cover of snow by the morning of the 26th. The daytime temperature reached 11.2°C (12.7°C Bridge of Allan) on a sunny 29th.

March   Dry and generally cold

Over the first six days there was fresh sunny weather with night frosts. The air temperature reached 13.4°C (14.5°C Bridge of Allan) on the 3rd but it fell to –3.7°C (–5.0°C Bridge of Allan) by the morning of the 5th. From the 7th onwards, an easterly airstream brought in cold damp air from continental Europe with poor visibility. There was heavy continuous rain over 48 hours from the 11th, which turned to snow by midday on the 12th. The 48-hour precipitation total was 35.4 mm (31.5 mm Dunblane, 42.6 mm Bridge of Allan). By late evening on the 12th, snow had accumulated to a depth of 3 cm or more and lay for the next two days, which were bitterly cold in a fresh ESE wind. The average daytime maximum temperature between the 12th and 14th was only 2.7°C (2.4°C Bridge of Allan). After the 15th, Scotland was again affected by a cold damp easterly airstream and the weather was very dull, with low cloud and occasional drizzle, up to the 23rd. Under clearing skies, night temperatures fell below freezing, reaching –2.8°C on the 24th (–4.0°C Bridge of Allan). The wind then turned towards the north, the weather became fresher and days were sunny, with excellent visibility. Dry and cold easterly winds dominated the month resulting in rainfall 50% of average and mean temperature 1.7°C below average.

April   Cold at first; becoming warmer but very wet

The weather was very settled over the first seven days. Sunny periods developed under clearing skies but night temperatures fell below freezing on the 6th/7th (–2.0°C on 6th). Cloud and rain moved in from the west on the 8th but the next three days were much warmer. By the 11th there was drier weather over the east coast, but the west remained wet. The 12th was an unpleasantly cold, wet and raw day, the temperature rising only to 4.9°C (3.5°C Bridge of Allan and Dunblane). There were flurries of snow on the 13th but amounts of precipitation remained relatively small. More rain fell after the 15th and the 48-hour total over the 16th and 17th was 22.2 mm (19.5 mm Dunblane). The weather then remained very unsettled and snow fell in thundery showers on the 19th. The temperature rose briefly on the 20th and 21st in a warm southerly airstream. There was a clear and dry spell on the 25th but less settled weather with heavy showers and sunny spells persisted to the end of the month.

May Cold and dry at first, then warmer and wetter later

The wind was north-easterly over the first three days, which were cool and clear. The temperature fell to –2.0°C (–2.6°C Bridge of Allan; –2.9°C Dunblane) by the morning of the 3rd. While the weather remained cold, the snowline on the local hills remained at 400 m. After the 7th there were two days of calmer clear weather before the north-easterly breeze returned on the 10th. The 11th was a gusty day with intermittent rain, which fell as sleet or snow over higher ground. The air became warmer overnight on the 12th/13th and by 0900 GMT on the 13th the temperature had already reached 13.8°C in Bridge of Allan. Under a light south-westerly breeze and an almost cloudless sky, the maximum temperature eventually reached 18.3°C on the 14th (22.0°C Bridge of Allan). The north-easterly breeze paid another visit on the 15th and the temperature fell back to unseasonally low levels again for several days. The 22nd was wet and windy (14.3 mm). By the third week of the month the national press was announcing that May had been the coldest since records began in 1659! The 28th was another very wet and windy day (13.0 mm; 13.9 mm Bridge of Allan, 14.5 mm Dunblane). The north of Scotland experienced a severe south-westerly gale on the 31st but winds in the Forth Valley, while strong, did not reach gale-force.

June Warm and dry

Over the first eleven days there was generally unsettled weather but there were some long sunny spells. From the 5th onwards the wind changed to southerly which was very warm and humid and the daytime temperature topped 20°C locally on the 6th. Heavy showers occurred overnight on the 7th/8th, which were thundery in some parts of Britain. The temperature fell on the 10th and the wind became fresh to strong westerly. Rain fell for much of the 11th and was exceptionally heavy during the afternoon. The 24-hour rainfall was 13.5 mm (11.3 mm Dunblane). More settled weather developed on the 12th and the next four days were bright and sunny, reaching 24.2°C on the 16th (25.8°C Bridge of Allan). The weather remained warm and dry, although night temperatures fell quite sharply, reaching 2.6°C by the morning of the 21st. There were three very hot days from the 22nd, reaching 27.3°C in Bridge of Allan on the 24th. There was continuous rain late on the 27th, after which the weather remained unsettled up to the end of the month.

July Mostly warm and quite dry

Over the first four days the weather was unsettled, with heavy showers and spells of more persistent rain. On the 5th, a fresh to strong WNW breeze developed and there were lengthy sunny spells over the next few days before a falling cloud-base and fine drizzle arrived on the 10th. The weather remained cloudy, but daytime temperatures managed to top 20°C on the 12th and 13th. Calm settled weather then persisted until the 20th. Between the 15th and 18th an easterly sea-breeze developed during afternoons, suppressing temperatures a little, but in its absence, the temperature on the 19th and 20th exceeded 25°C. The hot spell was brought to an end on the 21st and continuous heavy rain arrived on the 22nd (15.5 mm; 15.2 mm Bridge of Allan). This cleared away slowly on the 23rd, and the 24th was warm, sunny and fresh, but rain returned on the 25th.

August Warm with rain later

Showers fell in a fresh south-westerly breeze over the first two days before a warm southerly airstream became established on the 4th. However, while daytime temperatures topped 20°C on most days, cloud tended to be ever-present and conditions were often rather dull. After the 8th there were steadily increasing amounts of rain and the 10th was a wet day (9.8 mm; 11.8 mm Bridge of Allan, 13.0 mm Dunblane). Parts of the Gleneagles Golf Course became flooded for a short while. From the 12th, there was a spell of dry and very warm weather until the 19th, when the maximum temperature reached 25.3°C. Rain was falling by the late afternoon of the 19th, heralding a spell of unsettled weather. Rain fell as heavy showers with thunder and lightning on the 23rd and the Borestone Bar in St Ninians was struck by lightning, which set the roof on fire. There were further spells of rain over the next few days until more settled weather regained a foothold on the 28th, resulting in a sunny and dry last few days.

September Warm and exceptionally dry

On the 1st, rain fell over Scotland in a very light south-westerly breeze after which the daytime temperature rose quickly, reaching 23.5°C (25.2°C Bridge of Allan). However, conditions were very dull at times with low cloud and poor visibility. A cold easterly airstream on the 5th pulled the maximum temperature down to 14.9°C. After the 6th, warm dry weather returned until the 10th, although the light winds still came from an easterly direction. Under relatively clearer skies, night temperatures began to fall, resulting in heavy morning dew and occasional ground fog around dawn. Cloud increased and the easterly breeze freshened to become strong overnight on the 11th/12th. Dry weather continued between the 13th and 16th before the easterly wind returned again. Cloud cover increased after the 20th which brought an end to almost three weeks without measureable rainfall. The 24th was the first of the truly wet days after the dry spell, and there were more substantial rainfalls over the following days. The wind became strong south-westerly on both the 26th and 28th, and there was heavy driving rain overnight on the 28th/29th (10.0 mm). The weather remained unsettled for the rest of the month, in a showery south-westerly airstream.

October Warm and very wet

The weather for most of the month was dominated by a succession of rainy days which totalled 25 by the end of the month, but the air temperature was well above the seasonal average. The first two days were calm and almost cloudless but there was a strong south-westerly wind and heavy rain overnight on the 2nd/3rd. The wind remained in the west over the following days, which were wet with some lengthy sunny spells. There were calmer conditions between the 8th and 10th and, during breaks in the cloud cover, the night temperature reached –0.1°C in Bridge of Allan by the morning of the 8th (grass minimum –1.0°C). Further unsettled weather, with spells of heavy continuous rain and strong winds then persisted almost unabated until the 21st. The 14th and 15th were particularly wet, the 48-hour fall being 31.1 mm. Night temperatures fell during breaks in the cloud cover on the 21st but unsettled weather resumed on the 23rd, with more rain in fresh to strong winds. Former hurricane Lili crossed the British Isles between the 27th and 29th and was centred off south-west Scotland by midday on the 28th, which was a wild and wet day, and the Allan eventually overtopped its banks. The wind was very strong in central Scotland, resulting in some structural damage. The 48-hour rainfall over the 27th and 28th amounted to 30.2 mm.

November Cold and quite wet, with snow later

Unsettled, wet and windy weather continued over the first eight days and westerly winds reached gale-force in many places. There was heavy rain and severe gales overnight on the 5th/6th. After the storm had passed, the 7th was a calm and sunny day, but night temperatures then fell substantially below freezing for the first time, reaching –3.0°C in Dunblane. The wind had veered towards the north by the 11th at the start of what was to be a protracted spell of generally cold weather, heralded by the appearance of a capping of snow above 600 m on local hills. The 18th dawned calm and exceptionally cold under a cloudless sky, the temperature having fallen to –4.7°C (–6.8°C Bridge of Allan). The daytime temperature on the 19th reached only 3.0°C (1.5°C Dunblane). Heavy wet snow, with very large flakes, began falling after 08.00 GMT on the 21st, which had accumulated to more than 10 cm by midday. The snow became showery and began to turn to sleet by the afternoon. The 24-hour equivalent rainfall was 20.4 mm. As the clouds cleared, the night temperature fell below freezing and by the morning of the 22nd up to 5 cm of crusted frozen snow lay on the ground. This thawed a little during the day but refroze at night. The 24th was a miserably cold day with persistent sleet, which turned to snow later and the maximum temperature reached only 1.4°C in Bridge of Allan. Snow lay to a depth of 3 cm or more by the morning of the 25th and a succession of moderate to severe night frosts ensured that frozen snow lingered until the end of the month, despite some daytime thawing.

December Cold and rather dull

There was wind and rain on the 1st (15.2 mm), followed by a brisk westerly on the 2nd. On the 3rd there was further rain, which turned to snow in a freshening northerly wind (16.5 mm; 14.9 mm Bridge of Allan). The temperature began to fall in a cold north-westerly on the 5th, the cloud cover clearing to allow night temperatures to fall sharply and by the 6th, the temperature had fallen to –7.5°C. Scotland was then affected by mild air which gave very dull weather with a low cloud base until the 12th. The night minimum on the 9th fell to only 7.0°C. Colder air and night frosts returned on the 12th but milder air from the 14th took daytime temperatures over 9.0°C for three consecutive days. There was heavy overnight rain on the 17th, which continued through the day on the 18th (48-hour total 25.1 mm; 33.5 mm Dunblane). A cold easterly airstream then developed which limited the daytime temperature to 4.8°C on the 19th. Settled weather extended over Scotland on the 20th for three days, which brought bright sunny weather but a return to night frosts. Cloud increased late on the 23rd and the Christmas period was dull and cold. Rain fell late on the 26th, but as the cloud cleared, night temperatures again fell below freezing. By the afternoon of the 30th, snow was beginning to fall in a freshening north-easterly. The last day of the year brought further snow showers and the daytime temperature rose to only 2.0°C in Bridge of Allan (0.0°C Dunblane).

WEATHER NOTES

Heavy snow in February

As warmer Atlantic air pushed very slowly eastwards into cold polar continental air on the 5th, snow began to fall. Snow was already falling in the Stirling area by dawn on the 5th and it continued for the rest of the day and on into the 6th. The leading edge of the snow was exceptionally slow moving and the southerly wind gusted to very strong, particularly in exposed places. By dawn on the 6th, more than 50 cm had accumulated over higher ground and drifts of 2 to 3 m were reported. The region worst affected by the snow was Dumfries and Galloway where a state of emergency was declared. Local opinion was that conditions were the worst they had experienced for at least 30 years, and comparisons were made with the snows of February 1947. It proved impossible to keep the A(M)74 open and many vehicles were stranded

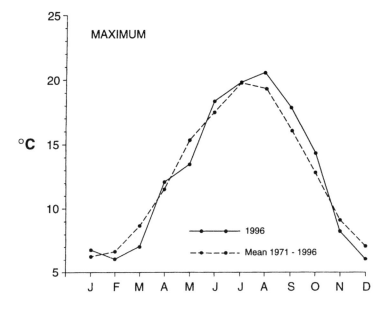

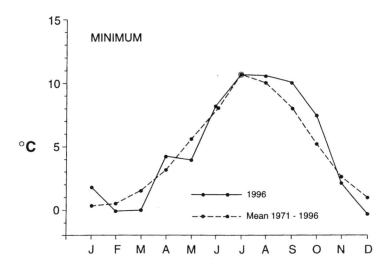

Figure 1. Monthly air temperatures (maximum and minimum) at Parkhead II 1996.

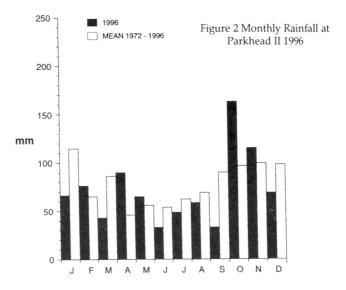

Figure 2 Monthly Rainfall at Parkhead II 1996

for up to 24 hours near Beattock. As many as 1,000 motorists were affected. Snow also brought down power lines and more than 25,000 homes were without electricity. All schools in south-west Scotland were closed. The army was called in to rescue the stranded and to take supplies to outlying settlements. On the railways, sixteen passengers were stranded when the 07.09 GMT Stranraer to Glasgow train became stuck in a 5 m drift four miles south of Barrhill. The coastguard helicopter from Belfast was called in to airlift the passengers to a local hotel. Elsewhere, trains on the West Coast Main Line were delayed by up to five hours.

The gale of May 31st

A deepening depression (984 mb) lay 300 miles off the coast of south-west Ireland at 06.00 GMT on the 30th. During the course of the day it drifted slowly north-eastwards and by midnight it had moved to a position 100 miles west of the Hebrides where the central pressure had fallen to 974 mb. As the depression moved northwards and continued to deepen, reaching 971 mb by 12.00 GMT on the 31st, the wind to the south of its centre strengthened to severe south-westerly gale-force over much of northern Scotland. The strong winds persisted all day but had abated to a strong breeze in most places by midnight. During the course of the day a double-decker bus loaded with school children was blown off the road on Slocht summit south of Inverness and clouds of dust were blown off dry fields bringing poor visibility along the main Aberdeen to Inverness road. Lossiemouth meteorological station recorded several hours of blowing sand during the afternoon. A postal van was blown off the road on Harris, and ferry traffic was disrupted in the Shetlands.

A dry September

The weather during much of September was dominated by high pressure and winds from a dry easterly direction. This was most marked between the 2nd and 21st. The average atmospheric pressure in Bridge of Allan (09.00 GMT) was 1018.0 mb but on 17 days the pressure was greater than 1020 mb. Over the British Isles as a whole, rainfall was well below average almost everywhere and it was the driest September since 1986. In south-east England it was the driest since 1959. In the Stirling area there were 21 consecutive days without measureable rainfall, which was matched by similar dry spells elsewhere. Over Scotland, the greatest shortfalls were generally in the east, Leuchars (Fife), for example, receiving only 30% of the 35-year average for the month. The figures in the west were only marginally better, but Stornoway managed to reach 64% of the average.

Mountain snows of Scotland

Habitats which are sensitive to the persistence of snow cover in montane environments have been identified as favourable for conservation under the EC Habitats Directive. In recent years, changes have occurred in the Scottish climate during the winter months. These have been, with some exceptions, warmer and wetter than in previous decades, and winds have been more frequently from a westerly direction. This has led to changes in the location and persistence of snowbeds in the Scottish Highlands. Snow persistence arises as a result of a combination of favourable site (aspect, altitude, topographic shelter) and weather (airflow, intensity of precipitation, heat and moisture advection) conditions. Research is planned which will explore the relationship between snowbed location and site and weather variables. Identification of snowbed locations at fixed points in time will be based initially on the personal field records made by Mr J M Pottie (Inverness) who has detailed the locations and persistence of snowbeds on Ben Wyvis and Braeriach since 1974.

Automatic weather station at the University

Some while ago the University was approached by *Westwind* of Telford New Town in Shropshire with a view to adopting Stirling as a location for one of a UK-wide network of automatic weather stations. A Davis Weather Wizard III has been installed on one of the service towers above 'A' corridor in the Cottrell Building. The equipment monitors wind speed and direction, rainfall and temperature, which are displayed in the Environmental Science soils laboratory. The system is connected to the phone network which means that

Westwind can interrogate the data at any time. At the Stirling end, a manual record is currently kept of conditions at 09.00 GMT but plans are in hand to use the telephone connection to transfer the weather data into a datafile in the climatology laboratory. After processing, an ongoing summary of the previous week's weather will then be made available on the campus information network.

Acknowledgement

This paper is based on the Annual Climatological Bulletin which is published by the Department of Environmental Science at the University of Stirling.

REVIEWS (Naturalist)

Ardentallen – land use history of an Argyll peninsula. D. N. McVean. *The Scottish Naturalist* 108, pp3-105. 196.

This study of an oakwood area, south of Oban, is also available as a separate from the author, and Craignish Conservation Trust. It was originally offered to FNH but routed to Dr Gibson of *The Scottish Naturalist*. It is a salutory 'failure' story, a sound land management project, frustrated by nature and an unsympathetic landowner.

The Rhossdhu House Reindeer Antlers. John Mitchell. *Glasgow Naturalist* 23(2), p49. 1997.

A short paper on this Ice Age historic discovery of 1935, with photo.

L.C.

FORTH AREA BIRD REPORT 1996

C. J. Henty

Yet more contributors appear this year. Notable records include several Smew and Marsh Harriers and an exhausted Manx Shearwater at Killin in June. On the estuary there were 252 Great Crested Grebes in February and a Great Northern Diver in December. There was a fair autumn passage of Curlew Sandpipers and Ruffs whilst in spring Turtle Dove, Yellow Wagtail, and Lesser Whitethroat all appeared in possible breeding habitats though with no indications of nesting. Unusual birds do appear away from the coast – the third record of Black Redstart was on the Thornhill carse in late autumn. Stonechats have decreased, as feared, after the severe frost in December 1995.

This report is compiled from a larger archive of records submitted to the local recorder under the national scheme organised by the Scottish Ornithologists Club. The area covered by the report comprises the council areas of Falkirk and Clackmannan together with Stirling, excluding Loch Lomondside and other parts of the Clyde drainage basin. Please note that we do not include the Endrick water, i.e. Fintry and Balfron. Records from Carron Valley may be published both here and in the report on Clyde birds. The inland part of Falkirk is once more neglected and the extensive and often inaccessible hills in the north of our area have had only sporadic coverage.

Some good conservation news is that Cambus Pools were greatly extended in 1997, the work being sponsored by Distillers Company in their Water of Life scheme. The new areas of shallow water will need time for vegetation and animal life to become established, the eventual effect on birds will be watched with keen interest.

The 1996 weather started with frequent frosts and occasional snow through a dull January and a sunny February. Early March was cold with snow in mid-month and ended with a cold, sunny period that extended into April, though the end of that month provided much rain. May was generally cold with snow laying above 400 m, eventually becoming wet and windy. Most of June and July were warm and dry whilst in August hot weather alternated with heavy rain. September was mainly dry but ended with strong winds and rain; this continued through October and into November, then becoming much colder with snow. The unsettled but cold conditions continued through December with Christmas being notably dull and cold.

Most information on the breeding numbers of common species come from two studies of mapped territories. One is a Common Birds Census plot east of Doune, this is 87 Ha of undulating, dry-field farmland at about 70 m a.s.l, mixed pasture and winter cereal, which is referred to as "Doune CBC" in text. The other is a Waterways Birds Survey along 5 km of the R.Devon at Alva which has much damp scrub surrounded by mixed pasture and arable, referred to as "Devon WBS", or, for species that are not fully mapped, as "5 km of lower Devon". For less common species I can sometimes mention data in terms of the numbers of pairs or apparently occupied territories for particular locations. Several observers send in a list largely or entirely for their home locality, much of this information is not appropriate for these annual reports but it is valuable to have on record and I am keeping them in a special file. At the moment there are fourteen such lists referring to the whole district from Falkirk to Killin.

For many species the records sent in are very unrepresentative of their general distribution, this applies particularly to very common species or to those that are secretive or breed in inaccessible places. Readers can consult the the Check List published in the Forth Naturalist and Historian vol 15, but in addition I have in this report put, after the species name, a coded summary of general distribution – which often apparently contradicts the detailed records that are published for the year.

B - Breeding status, widespread (in more than five 10 km squares)
b - "   "   , local, scarce (in fewer than five 10 km squares)
W - Winter status, widespread or often in groups of more than ten.
w - "   "   , local, scarce (local and usually fewer than ten in a group)
P - Passage (used when species is usually absent in winter, P or p used for widespread or local as in winter status)
S or s - present in summer but does not normally breed, widespread or local.

Thus BW would be appropriate for Robin, B for Swallow, p for Ruff and SW for Cormorant. No status letter is used if a species occurs less than every other year.

An asterix (*) in front of the species name means that all records received have been quoted.

The SOC has pressed for a more systematic vetting of records of species that are unusual locally, this area now has an informal panel of five – C. Henty (Recorder), W. Brackenridge (Dep. Recorder), J. Crook (local SOC rep), A. Blair and D. Thorogood. The judging of national UK or Scottish rarities continues as before, but we have produced for the upper Forth a list of species that are scarce locally and where the records need to be supported by either a full description or sufficient evidence to remove any reasonable doubt. This list and a background explanation have been circulated to a hard core of observers and can be got from the recorder at SOC meetings or by post. Any species which is a vagrant to the area, and most of those which are asterisked in this report, will come into this category.

The organiser for the inland waters part of the national wildfowl counts (WEBS), has made available an account of the results for the winter 1996-1997. These often contribute to the species accounts and there is also a separate summary at the end of the report which concentrates on localities.

There is an ever-increasing amount of information coming in: records on the standard species cards need only to be sorted and I would urge observers to use these wherever possible (putting as many records for one species on a single card); records on sheets, whether written, hand-typed or computer-typed, need to be either retyped onto a computer database or cut and pasted onto species sheets. This is time consuming and the recorder can no longer do this systematically without extensive help from contributors; otherwise these records will be scanned on arrival and only those items seeming to be salient will be transferred to the database, all the original sheets will be kept on file but that information is very difficult to unearth and inevitably some uncopied records will in fact be important but remain hidden. Appeals for assistance will continue!

The following abbreviations have been used : AoT - apparently occupied territory, BoA - Bridge of Allan, c/n - clutch of n eggs, BBS - Breeding Birds Survey, CBC- Common Birds Census, CP - Country Park, F - Female, GP - gravel pit, J - juvenile, L. - Loch, NR - Nature Reserve, M - Male, ON - on nest, Res - Reservoir, SP - summer plumage, V - Valley, WBS - Waterways Bird Survey, WG - Wildlife Garden, Y - young.

This report has been compiled from records submitted by: P. & M. Ashworth, A. Ayre, M. Adam, M. Anderson, B. W. Barker, M. V. Bell, N. Bielby, Birdline Scotland, A. Blair, W. R. Brackenridge, R. A. Broad, G. J. Brock, D. M. Bryant, G. Bryson, D. J. Cameron, R. Chapman, D. A. Christie, K. Dodds, A. Downie, D. S. Fotheringham, A. H. Haddow, M. Hargreave, S. Harley, J. G. Harrison, S. Haysome (SHs), C. J. Henty, T. Jacobs, R. Jones, H. Kerridge, J. G. Leisk, A. K. McNeil (AKM), J. Mallett, J. Marshall (JMr), W. McEwan, A. McKillop, J. Mitchell, R. L. Nudds, D. Orr-Ewing, G. Owens, H. M. Rankine, D. Rees, H. Robb, P. W. Sandeman, S. Sankey, R. Shand, A. Smith, W. G. Smith, P. Stirling-Aird, A. Tewnion, D. Thorogood, A. Thiel, B. R. Thomson, M. Trubridge, J. Wheeler, I. Wilson, M. Wilson, R. Youngman.

Thanks are due to the Deputy Recorder, W. R. Brackenridge, for assistance and advice on records, to A. Thiel for putting a batch of records on computer and for analysing wader data, to Dr S. J. Harrison for a copy of the Annual Climatological Bulletin (1995), to P. Stirling-Aird for data from the Raptor Study Group, and to Dr M. V. Bell for assessing the counts of geese.

SYSTEMATIC LIST

Codes - S, F and C indicate records from Stirling, Falkirk and Clackmannan "Districts".

RED-THROATED DIVER *Gavia stellata (b,w)*
F   1 Blackness 4 Feb & 27 Dec; 1 Bo'ness 28 Jan; 2 Kinneil 7 Jan, 1 on 21st & 3 on 4 Feb, 1 on 28 Dec; 2 Skinflats 3 Jan, 1 on 2 & 29 Feb, 1 found dead 13 Apr; 1 on 8 & 21Dec. 1 Higgins Neuk 20 Nov (AB AS CJH DMB MVB DF GO DT).
C   1 Kennetpans 21 Jan & 1 Tullibody Inch on 28th (CJH DMB).
S   3 pairs & a single bird seen on 4 lochs in breeding season, no young seen, 1 pair nested but failed (WRB). Singles on Forth at Drip Carse

7 Jan & L.Laggan on 10th & 11th, L.Iubhair 3 Feb, L.Ruskie 16 Mar, Lake of Menteith 27 Mar (DAC RC CJH NB).

BLACK-THROATED DIVER   *Gavia arctica (b,w)*
F   Blackness: 1 on 10 Jan & 2 on 25th, 1 on 18 Nov & 27 Dec; 2 Carriden 9 Dec; 1 Kinneil 3 Feb & 2 on 4th; 2 Skinflats 3 Jan (AB DMB MVB CJH RS).
S   Up to 4 pairs seen on 3 lochs in breeding season, no young seen, 2 pairs nested but failed (RAB WRB DAC NB). 1 Cocksburn Res 26 Jan (AT) & 1 L.Earn 27 Dec (NB). *Inland records unusual in winter, Ed.*

*GREAT NORTHERN DIVER   *Gavia immer*
F   1 Kinneil 8 Dec (DMB).

LITTLE GREBE   *Tachybaptus ruficollis (B,w)*
F   A few in autumn-winter on or near estuary, also Black Loch, Little Denny Res. (AB NB GO DT).
C   1 Cambus Pools 12 May (CJH). 2 Kersiepow Ponds 26 Oct (NB).
S   At Airthrey 2 pairs fledged 1+3Y after many attempts (MVB) - however, 7 juv seen here on 6 Oct (KD). 2 pairs bred Cocksburn Res, only 2 juv seen in Sep-Oct (AT). As usual regular on wildfowl counts on highland lochs, max 7 L.Lubnaig 20 Mar & 8 L.Voil 27 Nov (NB).

GREAT CRESTED GREBE   *Podiceps cristatus (b,W)*
F   2 in SP Black Loch 4 Mar (NB). 44 Blackness 10 Jan & 15 on 27 Dec. Kinneil monthly max: Jan 110, Feb 253, Mar 128, Apr 36, May 1, Jun 5, Jul 42, Aug 16, Sep 34, Oct 13, Nov ?, Dec 60 (AB MVB CJH DT AS). Skinflats max 11 on 8 Dec (MVB AB). 1 (1st) Little Denny Res 8 Nov (NB).
C   6 Gartmorn 1 Feb & 8 on 22 Nov (WRB AT).
S   Pair Cocksburn Res from 29 Feb, nested but eggs deserted in June probably due to disturbance (AT). At Carron Valley Res 2 on 25 Feb, 2 pairs raised 2+3 Y (DAC WME JM). 1 Lake of Menteith 16 Jan, 13 in BP on 27 Mar with 3 pairs in Apr-May; 9 (1Juv) on 17 Sep, 1 on 10 Nov (NB DAC). 1 L.Watston 10 Mar (CJH). 6 L.Coulter 16 Sep (possibly bred); 1 North Third Res 14 Feb & 8 Nov; 1 L.Venachar 28 Feb, 2 on 10-13 Nov & 1 on 16 Dec (DAC NB). Pair with 2 Juv Vale of Coustry (Blairdrummond) 5 Sep, 7 & 9 Oct (NB).

*SLAVONIAN GREBE   *Podiceps auritus*
F   1 Kinneil 7 Jan (AB).
S   1 (BP) Carron Valley Res 27 Jun (HK) & 1 on 5 Oct (AKM).

FULMAR   *Fulmarus glacialis (p)*
F   Kinneil: 3->NW 20 Apr (AB). 12->W 9 Jun, 36 records to 24 Aug & 8 more to 29 Sep (DT GO). 1 dead Skinflats 2 Feb (GO), 6 on 9 Jun (DMB).
S   1 Airthrey 13 Jun (DMB). 1 over Bridge of Allan 22 Aug (L.Johnston).

*MANX SHEARWATER *Puffinus puffinus*
S   1 Killin 6 Jun, ringed Skomer 27/8/94; found exhausted, later released (per RSPB).

GANNET *Sula bassana (p)*
F   Kinneil: 50 on 21 Sep, mainly ->W, 74% juv (DT). Also 22 records of Juvs 9 Sep to 26 Oct of which 8 at Skinflats flew W inland (DT AB GO).

CORMORANT *Phalacrocorax carbo (S,W)*
F   32 Bo'ness 15 Sep. 120 Skinflats 3 Jan & 73 on 8 Dec. 64 Higgins Neuk 21 Dec (CJH MVB DF).
C   94 S.Alloa roost 4 Feb, 60 Tullibody Inch 18 Sep (CJH). 8 Gartmorn 13 Dec (AT).
S   18 Lake of Menteith 4 Feb & 29 on 13 Oct (RAB NB). Regular in winter on upper Forth: 13 at Teith confluence 4 Feb, 16 there to 6 km upstream 16 Dec, 6 Gargunnock- Kippen 10 Mar (RC AMK MT). Max at Airthrey 5 on 20 Dec. 7 Carron Valley Res 3 Dec (AT).

GREY HERON *Ardea cinerea (B,W)*
F   19 Skinflats 15 Sep (MVB). 8 Kinneil 8 Sep (GO). 14 Airth 27 Feb (CJH).
C   11 on R.Devon at Tillicoultry 23 Mar (RN). 11 Tullibody Inch 18 Sep (CJH).
S   34 used nests Blairdrummond (Nyadd) 27 May (CJH). 45 L.Venachar 20 Feb (DJC). 10 Lecropt 21 Dec (MVB).

MUTE SWAN *Cygnus olor (B,W)*
     WEBS max total of 232 in Oct (NB)
F   2 Pairs, 1 nest at East Grangemouth 28 Apr (DT). On Union Canal: 26 Bonnybridge 1 Mar, 14 Brightons 14 Sep (AA JW).
C   3 Pairs + 4J Gartmorn 6 Jul, 18 (4J) on 22 Nov (DAC AT). 1 nest fledged 2 at Cambus, 2 pairs on 21 Apr, 7 Sep & 12 Nov (CJH WRB). 26 (10 imm) on Devon WBS 4 May, Pair reared 2Y there + Pair with 3Y from downstream on 14 Jun; nested Kersiepow, 6Y on 21 May (CJH NB).
S   37 Lake of Menteith 26 Mar, 2 nests on 29 Apr. Pair + 3J Gartmore 15 Sep (DAC NB). Pair + 3Y Culcreuch 7 Jul (DAC). Pair at Airthrey reared 8 out of 9Y (MVB). At Cromlix 20 Sep, pair with 5J at Lodge Pond & pair with 4J at House Pond. 7 (3J) Vale of Coustry (Blairdrummond) 5 Sep. Pair with 3J Little Denny Res 16 Sep (NB). 14 on Blairdrummond/Drip Carse 6 & 10 Apr (DT IW).

WHOOPER SWAN *Cygnus cygnus (W)*
     WEBS max total of 104 in Nov (NB)
F   1 Grangemouth 26 Apr (JW). 1 adult (yellow ring) Kinneil 26 Jul & 29 Sep, 8 -> W 20 Oct (AB DT). 6 (4J) Skinflats 26 Oct (MVB GO) & 6-> SE Higgins Neuk 20 Nov (DF). 5 Bonnybridge 13 Jan & 9 on 14 Dec (MA).
C   2 Gartmorn 14 Jan (DT); 6 there on 6 Oct & 6 Cambus on 30th (WRB). *Scarce Clacks this year, Ed.*
S   Widespread on highland lochs, max :19 (10J) L.Dochart 2 & 21 Feb &

35 (11J) 28 Dec, 14 L.Lubnaig 2 Feb (NB DAC DT MT). 10 (3J) Carron Valley Res 3 Nov (AT).
Records of up to 20 on Drip/Blairdrummond Carse Jan to 23 Mar probably all refer to one herd but 27 (6J) Thornhill 4 Feb seem distinct (MT RC DAC RJ DT). Max of 44 on the whole Carse 28 Jan & 27 on 24 Feb (MVB). 32 flew over Lecropt till out of sight (SE to NW) on 2 Apr, presumably on spring departure (CJH).
1st of autumn heard over Thornhill 30 Sep (SS). 10 (6J) Killin 7 Nov & 22 on 27 Dec (PWS). 32 Thornhill Carse 5 Nov (TJ), otherwise scarce on Carse of Stirling, 16 on 15 Nov could account for total records (RC HK CJH).

PINK-FOOTED GOOSE Anser brachyrhynchus (W)
The Pinkfeet and Greylag Geese data have been summarised by Dr M. V. Bell, with additions by the Editor, from records of many observers ; the main counters were MVB, DMB, MC, NB, SS, MT, TJ, L.O'Toole.
3990 at Lecropt on 1 Jan had roosted on the river. 6700 were on Stirling Carse on 28 Jan but heavy snow in early Feb moved most of these birds on (2000 flew S & SW over Stirling on the 7th, DT) and numbers were low thereafter; a total of 2800 on 23 Mar was disappointing. 1200 were in the Alloa Inches area on 31 Mar, maybe part of 1985 at Kennetpans on the 5 Apr. Also in April 1700 at Lecropt on 2nd, whilst day and night flocks flew NW over Bridge of Allan on the 29th; the last big flock was 110 at Bandeath on 5 May, though a bird was over Airthrey on the 30th (DMB).
The only September record was of 23 flying SE over Kinneil on the 29th, then there were 1000 over Doune on 6 Oct and flocks of up to 300 moved W along the Gargunnock-Campsie scarp on 10th and 21st. Numbers were generally very low at all sites in the autumn. Skinflats was deserted on both the mid-October and November counts, though there were 432 there on 22 Oct and 400 on 29 Nov. There are a number of grey collared birds that have been marked at L.Leven on 12/10/94, one at Skinflats had been seen this year at Strathbeg on 8 Oct (AB GO). The steady rise in numbers over the last few autumns at Skinflats has stopped: the birds probably moved to Peppermill Dam due to disturbance from shooting, whilst 3057 were at Cowie on 19 Oct. There were 1280 at L.Mahaick on 13 Oct and 2700 there on the 16th, but none were recorded there later. None were found at L.Ruskie or Lake of Menteith on 13 Oct but there were 1200 on Flanders Moss on 12 Nov (not checked in Oct); no other roost site held birds in the Nov count since 1435 at the east end of Stirling carse roosted in Strathallan. Numbers on the carse remained low to the year end except for 4000 at Lecropt on 23 Nov (WRB).

BEAN GOOSE Anser fabalis (W)
F   Max around Slamannan 105 on 11 Feb, 35 in Avon valley may be extra; also 12 Crosshill 21 Jan (MA AD GO RS IW). 54 L.Ellrig 11 Oct, 117 nearby on 8 Nov & 127 on 6 Nov (NB). Note that mixed flocks can

occur: 64 with 32 Greylags and one Pinkfoot on 21 Dec (GO).

S   9 Carron Valley Res 29 Oct (GJB).

WHITE-FRONTED GOOSE *Anser albifrons (w)*

S   5 Kippen 28 Jan; 1 Lecropt 3 Feb & 1 on 24 Dec; 1 Thornhill Carse 3 Nov. (All identified subspecifically were Greenland race) (MVB DMB DT DR).

GREYLAG GOOSE *Anser anser* (b,W)

930 at Lecropt on 1 Jan was an exceptional flock for this site. A total of 1535 were found on the Carse on 28 Jan , but only 390 on 24 Mar. 105 L.Coulter on 17 Feb may be extra. An unusually large flock of Greylag (1720) was in the South Alloa/Kennetpans area on 21 Jan with 1200 still present on 31 Mar. Gartmorn had 600 on 18 Feb, probably part of the same flock. The discovery of a small flock in Glen Dochart was of particular interest with 62 on 18 Jan, 76 on 20 Mar and 60 on the 31st. Greylags were also scarce in autumn with none found on the weekend of the 12/13 Oct and only 505 on the Carse on 9 Nov plus 60 at Gart (Callendar). Visible migration included 14 high to the WSW at Stronend on 21 Oct.

CANADA GOOSE *Branta canadensis (b)*

    WEBS season total 232, 41 in Dec (NB).

F   4 Skinflats 10 Jun (AB).

C   At Gartmorn Jan-Feb, max 4 on 14 Jan (PMA WRB DT). 20 (with one Greylag) in Devon valley 2 Jun were presumably migrants (CJH).

S   32 Vale of Coustry (Blairdrummond) 23 Jan to 22 Mar, 24 on 7 Aug & 4 Dec, only 3 in Sep (NB). Pair + 2Y Hutchison 2 Jun (WRB). 8 L.Venachar Oct & Dec; 2 Thornhill Pond (newly made) Mar & Apr (NB DAC). A small bird with Pinkfeet at Lecropt 9 Nov (AD) *(possibly a nearctic migrant, record here in 1995, Ed).*

BARNACLE GOOSE *Branta leucopsis (w)*

F   Skinflats: 1 on 10 Feb; 3 on 22 Sep & 9 on 29th, last 4 on 25 Oct. Kinneil: 1 on 22 Jun - heavy wing moult but able to fly. 6 on 20 Sep, 8 flocks totalling 270 flew W or NW included 55 on 21st & 110 on 28th, last 4 on 25 Oct (DT SH AB DAC DMB GO RS).

S   On Carse of Stirling 2 on 28 Jan, 16 Sep to 24 Dec. 1 Cowie 19 Oct, 2 L.Watston on 23rd. Groups of 2 & 5 flew SW at Ashfield on 30 Sep & 20 Oct. (MVB RC DAC DT NB WRB)

*BRENT GOOSE *Branta bernicla*

F   12 at Skinflats 21 & 27 Jan were dark bellied (AB GO). 4 pale bellied at Kinneil on 29 Sep left W after brief stop (DT).

SHELDUCK *Tadorna tadorna (b,W)*

F   Winter max on Forth Estuary 374 on 18 Feb & 732 on 8 Dec. However the moult flock at Kinneil totalled 4750 on 17 Aug & there were 1095 at Skinflats on 15 Sep & 166 at Higgins Neuk on 23rd. 32 Skinflats 14 Jun, 1st broods at Kinneil on 22nd. Inland records: 1 Bonnybridge 2 Feb, 2 Dunmore Wood 10 May (MVB DMB CJH DF AA GB).

C   155 Tullibody Inch - Cambus 5 Apr & 120 on 7 Jul. Pair on Devon WBS 15 May but F found dead on 21st (DMB CJH).
S   3 Lecropt 5 Jan was unusual date for inland(IW).

WIGEON   *Anas penelope (b,W)*
        940 Forth Estuary 21 Jan 467 on 8 Dec (DMB). WEBS totals of 1076 in Dec (NB).
F   Kinneil: max 660 on 3 Jan, last 2 on 7 May; 1st of autumn 1 on 24 Aug, 700 on 26 Oct (MVB DT GO DMB)
C   800 Gartmorn 1 Feb. 900 Alloa Inch 28 Jan & 540 on 12 Dec, last at Cambus 3 May & return 13 Aug. F at Upper Glendevon Res 16 Jun (WRB BRT DMB CJH).
S   Max Gart Lochs (Cambusmore) 181 on 9 Nov. Other large loch counts included 102 L.Coulter 6 Dec & 65 L.Venachar on 16th. There are more on the upper Forth between the Teith and Kippen, max 438 between 2 to 10 Mar (NB RC MA MT).

*GADWALL   *Anas strepera*
F   1 Kinneil 3 Nov (DT).
S   3 Hutchison 15 Sep (WRB).

TEAL   *Anas crecca (B,W)*
        531 Forth Estuary 21 Jan & 609 on 8 Dec (DMB)
F   Kinneil: 300 on 21 Jan, last 6 on 7 May; visible arrival of 19 on 29 Aug that flew in from E and left W, 340 on 8 Dec. Pair Skinflats 13 Jun (DMB DT GO).
C   125 Alloa Inch 22 Sep & 140 on 12 Dec (DMB BRT). 68 on Devon, Alva-Dollar, 18 Jan; last, pair on 4 May. 2 Lower Glendevon Res 16 Jun. (NB RN CJH)
S   Max loch count, 113 L.Laggan 22 Nov (NB). Total of 108 on the upper Forth between the Teith and Kippen in early Feb (RC MT).

MALLARD   *Anas platyrhynchos (B,W)*
        398 Forth Estuary on 18 Feb & 601 on 8 Dec (DMB).
F   271 Skinflats 3 Jan. 211 Kinneil 3 Feb & 240 on 8 Sep (MVB AB DT)
C   17 AoT on Devon WBS (CJH). 265 Gartmorn 29 Dec (AT).
S   251 Airthrey 13 Feb & 226 on 20 Dec (MVB AT). At least 4 broods Cocksburn Res (AT). 333 Blairdrummond Safari Park 9 Oct (NB).

PINTAIL   *Anas acuta (W)*
F   Skinflats: 47 on 25 Feb & 52 on 24 Dec. Last Kinneil 5 on 13 Apr; 1st autumn on 31 Aug, max 9 on 29 Sep (AB GO DT). Pair Polmont 28 Jan (AA).
S   1 L.Lubnaig 18 Jan (NB).

Area Summary

Jan	Feb	Mar	Apr	-	Aug	Sep	Oct	Nov	Dec
54	50	33	16		1	18	17	2	58

Nb: only 1 count in Nov, main flock probably missed.

*GARGANEY   *Anas querquedula (p)*
F   4 (2 pairs) East Grangemouth 28 Apr (DT).

*SHOVELER *Anas clypeata (p)*
F   1 Skinflats 18 Feb & pair 31 Mar to 5 May (2 pair on 4th); 1 on 19 Sep.
      2 Grangemouth 28 Apr & 8 on 26 Oct. 2 Kinneil 24 Aug & 1 on 21 Sep
      (MVB GO AB DT DMB).
S   2 Lake of Menteith 17 Sep (NB)

POCHARD *Aythya ferina (W)*
C   18 Gartmorn 13 Dec (AT).
S   40 Carron Valley Res 23 Mar & 64 on 9 Nov (AB AKM). 31 Buckiesburn
      Res 14 Feb. Other counts over 20: 64 L.Katrine, 28 L.Ard & 22
      L.Venachar 24 Jan, 25 L.Achray 27 Feb, 25 L.Voil 21 Feb, 27 L.Coulter
      16 Sep, 31 L.Iubhair 30 Oct, 24 Killin Marshes 27 Dec, 31 L.Lubnaig 27
      Nov (NB).

TUFTED DUCK *Aythya fuligula (B,W)*
F   31 Little Denny Res & 57 Black Loch on 16 Sep (NB). 25 Grangemouth
      12 Jul (DT). Pair on Union Canal at Whitecross (Falkirk)12 May (JW).
C   2 pair + M on Devon WBS (CJH).
S   25 Airthrey 22 Mar (AT). 105 Carron Valley Res 15 Aug (RKP). 100
      L.Watston 30 Aug (DOE). 42 Coustry Lochs 5 Sep (NB). 21 on Forth
      above Stirling Bridge 15 Dec (AMK). 12 Cambusmore GP 12 Jun
      (PWS). Bred at Ashfield (8Y), Barbush (3Y), Torrie Lochan (3Y) (WRB
      BWB).

*SCAUP *Aythya marila (w)*
F   5 Kinneil 7 Jan, last a pair on 7 May; 3 on 29 Sep to 1 on 16 Oct. 11 (5M)
      Skinflats 6 Jan, 1 Carronshore 17 Mar (AB AS GO DT).
S   1 on Forth at Thornhill Carse 14 Feb (MT).

*EIDER *Somateria mollissima (w)*
F   1 Skinflats 3 Jan to 28 Apr (2 on 23 Mar). 3 (2M) Kinneil 7 to 20 Apr &
      1M to 12 May (MVB AB GO DT).

GOLDENEYE *Bucephula clangula (W)*
      67 Forth Estuary 18 Feb & 19 on 8 Dec (DMB)
F   16 Carron mouth 6 Jan, 16 Carronshore 2 Feb, 15 Skinflats 22 Dec. 11
      Kinneil 10 Mar (AB GO).
C   60 Gartmorn 31 Jan (WRB). 16 Tullibody Inch 6 Apr (CJH).
S   15 Carron Valley Res 17 Mar (WME). 64 (19M) Lake of Menteith on
      27 Mar, last 18 on 4 May. 16 L.Venachar 5 Apr & 17 on 27 Dec. 18 Killin
      7 Apr. 22 L.Dochart/Iubhair & 20 L.Lubnaig 27 Dec. (CJH NB DT). 50
      Cambuskenneth-Kildean 15 Dec (AT). 85 on Teith/Forth 5 Jan (IW). 12
      on upper Forth to Gargunnock 4 Feb (RC).

*SMEW *Mergus albellus (w)*
S   F L.Dochart 18 Jan, 21 Feb & 28 Apr (late) (NB WRB), 2F L.Iubhair 3
      Feb (DAC).

*LONGTAILED DUCK *Clangula hyemalis*
S   M at Lake of Menteith 27 Mar (CJH).

RED-BREASTED MERGANSER Mergus serrator (B,W)
      69 Forth Estuary 18 Feb & 50 on 8 Dec (DMB).
F   25 Skinflats 3 Jan & 31 on 18 Feb (MVB). 10 Kinneil as late as 13 Apr,
      16 on 12 & 26 Oct (AB GO). 27 Higgins Neuk 9 Dec (DF). Up to 4 on
      R.Carron at Larbert/Camelon 17 Feb to 23 Mar (MA GO).
S   17 on Forth at Stirling Bridge/Kildean 16 Nov (AMK) - this is not
      unusual but up to 4 occurred in Nov/Dec on Forth up to Gargunnock
      and on the Allan at BoA (RC AT), whilst a M at Callendar 18 Jan & one
      on L.Venachar 29 Dec (NB DAC) were unusual dates. In spring at
      Ashfield, Dunblane, L.Katrine (WRB NB). F+3Y Killin 12 Jul (PWS).

GOOSANDER Mergus merganser (B,W)
F   23 Black Loch 26 Feb (NB). 5 Skinflats 6 Jan & 6 on 15 Sep & 26 Oct; 3
      Kinneil 30 Mar & 1 on 22 & 30 Jun (MVB GO DT).
C   20 Tullibody Inch 6 Apr, 4 on 13 Aug. F+5Y Lower Glendevon Res 16
      Jun. (CJH WRB).
S   36 L.Ard 17 Sep, 30 L.Venachar 16 Aug, 64 Gart Loch 12 Oct, 20 Doune
      Ponds 26 Oct (NB DOE DAC). Totals on the upper Forth between the
      Teith and Kippen: 12 in Jan, 40 on 10 Mar; 12 on 16 Dec (MA RC MT).
      1 Airthrey 13 Nov & 15 Dec (DMB KD). In spring/summer noted at
      L.Ard (7Y), Thornhill (8Y), Lecropt (4Y) (WRB SS CJH).

*RUDDY DUCK Oxyura jamaicensis (b)
C   1 Gartmorn 14 Jan to 1 Mar, 1 on 6 Oct & 2 on 5 Dec (DT PMA WRB).
S   1M Doune Ponds Apr 13 (DAC).

RED KITE Milvus milvus
This year the RSPB extended the Red Kite reintroduction programme to
central Scotland. 19 wing and radio tagged birds were released on 1 Aug, by
12 Sep most birds had formed a communal roost but although supplied with
carrion only 8 were still around in December. These birds rarely move more
than 10 km from the roost site. Several birds have made made short
excursions, eg to Milngavie golf course, others have made longer and more
permanent movements: wintering in Dec in Ayrshire, Stranraer, Cumbria,
N.Yorkshire, Antrim. Good cooperation has been achieved from local farmers
and estate managers.(Abstracted from the RSPB Red Kite Newsletter 1996,
compiled by L. O'Toole and B. Etheridge).
S   Up to 7 seen in the release area from 15 Sep to 26 Nov (WRB NB).
C   1 Alva 22 Oct, flew W along Ochils scarp, mobbed by crows (PMA).
      This would seem to be the 1st modern record for Clacks, Ed.

*MARSH HARRIER Circus aeruginosus
F   Immature M Skinflats 25 May (AB GO).
SWP   F Thornhill 11 Aug (SS).

HEN HARRIER Circus cyaneus (b?, w)
      One definite nesting record; one coastal record. 24 males and 28
      Ringtails noted (Ed).
F   1 Black Loch 17 Oct (WRB). 1 Skinflats 1 Nov (AB).

S Pair raised 3Y Gargunnock Hills (MT). M Monachyle (Balquhidder) 24 Apr (AD). M Thornhill 3 Jul (SS). On Carse of Stirling 12 records 5 Jan to 1 Apr (3 together Lecropt on 2 Mar), at least 11 from 5 Oct to 24 Dec. On Braes of Doune & nearby, 4 records 12 Jan to 16 Mar & four 15 Sep to 7 Nov (IW CJH MA DMB MVB WRB DJC DAC KD DR MT DT NB). 1 Sheriffmuir 30 Apr & 31 Aug (DMB WRB). 2 Kippen Muir 11 Feb (DAC). 2 Flanders Moss 9 Feb, 1 on 26 Oct & 31 Dec (DOE DT).

SPARROWHAWK *Accipiter nisus (B,W)*
F At Skinflats through year, chased a Partridge on 4 Apr (AB GO). Pair Dunmore (GB).
C Through year at Cambus, in Apr-May Blairlogie (WRB DAC). Killed Collared Dove in Menstrie garden in Aug (BRT).
S Through year on Carse of Stirling and at Stirling and BoA, chased Sparrows in garden at Buchlyvie 13 Aug (MA AD TJ CJH DT DAC). At Mid-Torrie in May killed Sparrows inside a byre and a Wigeon in a wilfowl collection (BWB).

BUZZARD *Buteo buteo (B,W)*
As breeding bird: widespread SWP, scarce C, increasing S, no proof F.
F 7 Dunmore 10 Oct & 1 on 12 Dec (GB), 1 by M9 nearby (Kinnaird) 24 Feb to 12 Jul. 3 Kinneil 24 Aug, 2 on 8 Sep & 1 on 14th (DT). 2 Wallacebank Wood (Larbert) 5 Aug to 7 Dec (AS). 2 by R.Carron W of Larbert 14 Sep (MA). 1 Torwood 4 Feb & 3 on 26 May *(prob.Plean CP birds)*, 2 Cowie 2 Feb (AB MA). 1 Slamannan 3 Feb (JW).
C 1 AoT Dollar Jan to Nov (RN). 1 Alva Glen 29 Feb (CJH). 1 Cambus 28 Jan (DMB-*apparently 1st record for reserve*).
S In main breeding range to W & N, max soaring groups were 5 Buchlyvie Mar to Oct, 4 Buckie Glen 29 Mar & 4 Callendar 10 Mar (DAC CDJ). Wintered on Carse of Stirling, 2 to 1 Apr Arnieve (CJH) but 12 Lecropt 28 Jan & 13 on 11 Feb (DT). Around BoA, probably bred Kippenrait, 1 AoT Mine Wood Jul-Dec (AT CJH KD). 7 Loss Hill 31 Aug (WRB). 1 AoT Plean CP, 4 birds on 2 May (HMR).

GOLDEN EAGLE *Aquila chrysaetos (b,w)*
S 5 territories checked, all occupied by pairs; 2 successful pairs reared 2Y (PSA). No records outwith highlands.

OSPREY *Pandion haliaetus (p)*
C 1 Gartmorn 7 Jul, mobbed by Blackheaded Gulls (PMA).
S 1st seen Trossachs 31 Mar, last on 20 Aug (WRB). 1 Callander 7 May (DOE), 1->N Airthrey on 10th (MVB). 3 Carron V Res 4 Jul, last on 15 Aug (GJB).

KESTREL *Falco tinnunculus (B,W)*
Difficult to make significant observations, hence greatly underrecorded.
Only 4 records in 78 hours on Doune farm CBC (NB). Not noted on Devon WBS (CJH).

F   Through year at Skinflats (AB).
S   1 chased a Jay on Braes of Doune 4 Sep (NB).

*MERLIN   Falco columbarius (b?,w)
F   1 Kinneil 2 Mar, 1 Skinflats 24 Dec (GO). Pair on R.Carron at Bonnybridge 17 Nov (MA).
C   2 Glendevon 13 Nov (RJ).
S   Singles Blairdrummond Carse 9 Jan, Flanders Moss 9 Feb, Lecropt 10 Mar, Glengyle 12 Jun, Ashfield 20 Oct, Gargunnock 5 Dec & Callander 27 Dec (CJH DOE DT WRB DMB).

PEREGRINE   Falco peregrinus (B,W)
F   Most coastal records Jan-Feb & Jul-Dec, 1 Kinneil 30 Jun was odd date (DT).
C   2 territories checked, 2 pairs were successful rearing 5Y (PSA).
S   21 territories checked, 14 pairs + 3 apparent singles, 10 successful pairs reared 17Y (PSA). 2 Balquhidder 6 May killed a Goosander (DT). Seen on carse Jan, Mar, Oct-Dec (CJH DMB DR).

RED GROUSE   Lagopus lagopus (B,W)
        Generally under-recorded
S   In spring at L.Tinker, Cromlix, Upper Earlsburn Res, Cringate Muir (WRB DT GO). 13 + 6 Dumyat 31 Aug (WRB). 6 in 2 km of deep heather Muir Park 11 Jan (CJH).

PTARMIGAN   Lagopus mutus (b,w)
        No records received

*BLACK GROUSE   Tetrao tetrix (B,W)
        There are clearly leks that are not being visited.
S   12M Braeleny 23 Mar & 15M on 27 Apr (DOE CJH). 30M Bracklin Falls 27 Dec (DMB -largest group for years, Ed). M Glen Casaig 10 Dec. 2M L.Chon 13 Jun, 2 L.Arklet 11 May, 2F Ben Gullipen 23 Dec, 4 Sheriffmuir 7 May (CJH RAB WRB DJC SH). Display calls heard Ballochleam 5 Apr (DAC).

*CAPERCAILLIE   Tetrao urogallus (b,w)
SWP   F Braeval 3&7 May; M L.Ard forest drive 10 Dec (WRB DOE).

GREY PARTRIDGE   Perdix perdix (B,W)
F   12 Skinflats 21 Jul & 16 on 21 Dec (GO AB). Max 32 Kinneil 8 Aug to 28 Dec (RS et al). 2 pair bred Drumore (N.Doll) (GB). 14 Black Loch 6 Dec (NB). 40 Bogton (Bonnybridge) 15 Dec (MA - largest covey for years, Ed).
C   7 Cambus 10 Jan & 10 Kennetpans on 21st; 5+15 Alloa 22 Dec (WRB CJH BRT). 2 AoT on Devon WBS.
S   25 Drip Carse 4 Feb & 14 on 5 Dec (DT RJ).18 Blairdrummond Carse 19 Feb. 13 Thornhill 13 Nov (CJH). 10 Juv Kippen 11 Aug (DAC).

PHEASANT *Phasianus colchicus (B,W)*
Abundant (usually by releases) on fields next to keepered estates.
C Probably only 2 AoT on Devon WBS (approx. 1 km sq) (CJH).
S 20.4 AoT per km sq on Doune CBC- more than twice 1995 (NB).

*WATER RAIL *Rallus aquaticus (w)*
F 1 Kinneil 6 Sep (RS). 1 Skinflats 17 Oct (GO).
C 1 Cambus 13 & 20 Aug (WRB).

MOORHEN *Gallinula chloropus (B,W)*
F 1st chicks Kinneil 12 May, 10 on 29 Sep & 22 Dec (DT WRB CJH). 2 pairs nested Skinflats (AB). 8 Forth-Clyde canal Bonnybridge 1 Mar (AA). Max 6 Larbert House Loch 4 Mar to 8 Nov. 5 Little Denny Res 16 Sep (NB).
C 3 AoT Cambus in May, Ad+5Y 7 Jul, on nest 30 Aug (WRB). 2 AoT on Devon WBS (CJH).
S Airthrey: 20 on 25 Jan, 17 on 1 Dec; of 8 pairs only 3 successful, reared 5Y (AT MVB). Pair bred Torrie Lochan, 5Y (BWB). Pair bred Killin marshes, not seen till 10 Jun (PWS). 10 Blackdub floods 10 Jan. 5 Blairdrummond Safari Park pond Mar & Oct (NB). 8 on Forth floods, Abbey Craig, 15 Dec (AT).

COOT *Fulica atra (B,W)*
F 1 nest Kinneil. Pair + 2Y Skinflats 14 Jun (AB). 29 Little Denny Res 14 Feb, 70 on 6 Dec (NB).
C 2 AoT Cambus in May. 1 AoT on Devon WBS, did not nest (CJH). 300 Gartmorn 31 Jan & 455 on 13 Dec (WRB AT).
S Airthrey: 37 on 13 Feb; 9 prs with only 6Y fledged from 3 prs (MVB). 130 Lake of Menteith 16 Jan, 60 on 16 Mar & 268 on 13 Dec (NB DAC). 13 L.Watston 10 Mar (CJH). 27 Coustry Ponds 6 Sep. 26 Gart 22 Mar & 70 on 4 Dec. Pair bred Hillhead Pond (NB).

OYSTERCATCHER *Haematopus ostralegus (B,W)*
159 on Forth estuary 18 Feb & 126 on 8 Dec (DMB).
Spring return inland in February: over Stirling 21st, Ashfield 23rd, Alva 25th, also 210 Vale of Coustry 27th & 10 L.Venachar on 28th (DT WRB CJH NB).
F Kinneil: 270 on 28 Jul, 65 on 15 Dec, partial albino present through year to Nov (DT AB). Skinflats: 47 on 18 Feb, 20 on 29 Jun (AB MVB GO).
C 9 AoT Devon WBS (CJH).
S 70 Craigforth 25 Feb (DT). 148 by Forth, Gargunnock-Kippen, 10 Mar (MT). 140 Gart & 287 Coustry on 22 Mar. 17 AoT per sq km on Doune CBC (NB); 6 Cambusmore GP 8 Jun (CJH).

RINGED PLOVER *Charadrius hiaticula (b,W)*
F 75 Skinflats 30 May & 99 on 31st (RS GO). 52 Bo'ness 25 Dec (AS).
S 2 pairs Lower Earlsburn Res 31 Mar (DT). 3 Gart 27 Feb (NB). Pair Barbush GP 31 Mar, 2J in Jun (WRB). 4 Killin Marshes 7 Apr (CJH); 4 Breachlaich Quarry (Killin) 8 May - pair anxious (PWS).

*DOTTEREL   Charadrius morinellus
S   3 Balquhidder 10 May (per WRB).

GOLDEN PLOVER   Pluvialis apricaria (B,W)
        The small number of likely breeding records may indicate a reduction
        in range compared with twenty years ago. Passage in spring (inland)
        and October (especially by estuary) is well demonstrated (Ed).
F   30 Blackness 21 Jul (AS). Skinflats: 17 on 26 Jul, 185 on 28 Sep, 865 on
        26 Oct. Kinneil: 300 on 13 Oct, 400 on 3 Nov. 280 Kincardine Bridge 16
        Nov (GO DMB MVB DT).
C   1 Ben Buck 23 Jun (WRB).
S   75 (mainly Northern form) Blairdrummond Carse on 30 Mar & 70 on
        23 Apr (DT CJH). Pair Meall na Iolaire (Callander) 27 Apr (SS). 2 AoT
        Cam Chreag (Glen Lochay) 14 Jul (RY). 10 ->W Lecropt 19 Oct (DT).

GREY PLOVER   Pluvialis squatarola (W)
F   Very few on estuary in winter. 1 Kinneil 26 Jul. Skinflats: 1st of autumn
        25 on 10 Aug, 40 on 29 Sep, 31 on 25 Oct, 2 on 8 Dec (DT GO DMB AB
        MVB).
C   5 Tullibody Inch 22 Sep & 7 on 19 Oct (DMB WRB).

LAPWING   Vanellus vanellus (B,W)
F   Skinflats: 130 on 18 Feb; 480 on 17 Aug, 486 on 15 Sep, 1665 on 26 Oct;
        2 downy chicks on 23 May. 130 ->S Bo'ness 21 Aug. Kinneil: 440 on
        18 Jan; 70 on 21 Aug, 700 on 8 Sep & 1000 on 16th,1360 on 13 Dec; 1st
        chicks on 13 May (AB MVB CJH DT). 500 Higgins Neuk 21 Dec (DF).
        3 AoT N.Doll (GB).
C   992 Tullibody Inch on 18 Sep & 1100 on 22nd (CJH DMB).1 AoT
        Cambus Apr-May. 26 AoT Devon WBS (CJH).
S   Spring return to L.Mahaick & Coustry 27 Feb, L.Venachar on 28th,
        Ashfield 1 Mar. 209 by Forth, Gargunnock-Kippen, 3 Mar. 45 at Gart
        12 Oct were late for hill fringe sites. 4.8 AoT/ km sq on Doune CBC. 3
        pairs raised 3Y Barbush (NB WRB MT). 4F with Y Pendreich on 9 Jul
        (AT). 3 pairs with Y Killin Marshes 24 May (PWS). 164 Cambusmore 3
        Sep. Lecropt: 250 on 2 Oct & 1640 on 23rd, 800 on 21 Nov; 582
        Blackdub floods 7 Nov (CJH NB). 500 by Forth Kildean 16 Nov (AMK).

KNOT   Calidris canutus (W)
        5580 Forth Estuary 21 Jan & 2440 on 8 Dec (DMB).
F   4000 Bo'ness 21 Jan, 350 Blackness 11 Aug (DMB AS). Kinneil: 5500 on
        28 Jan, 2000 on 3 Feb & 500 on 9 Mar; 2 on 21 Jul, 15 on 9 Sep, 70 on
        10 Nov, 3000 on 29 Dec (DMB AB DT WRB). Skinflats: 1000 on 25 Feb,
        last on 31 May (AB GO). 163 Higgins Neuk 7 Jan & 170 Kennetpans 21
        Feb (DF CJH).

LITTLE STINT   Calidris minuta (p)
F   1st Kinneil on 20 Sep, max 10 on 27th, last 3 on 20 Oct. 3 Skinflats
        22 Sep & 2 Higgins Neuk on 23rd (GO DT DF).
C   2 Tullibody Inch 22 Sep (DMB).

S   3 Carron Valley Res 29 Sep (AKM).
Area Summary (half monthly)

Sept	Oct
0 20	0 3

CURLEW SANDPIPER *Calidris ferruginea (p)*
F   1st, Kinneil 1 on 15 Sep & Skinflats 3 on 18th, max 5 Skinflats on 29 Sep & last 1 Kinneil on 20 Oct (GO AB DT).
Area Summary (half monthly)

Sept	Oct
1 9	1 1

DUNLIN *Calidris alpina* (b?,W)
     8831 Forth Estuary 18 Feb & 5180 on 8 Dec (DMB).
F   Kinneil: 4500 on 28 Jan; 19 on 28 Jul, 135 on 1 Sep, 2300 on 28 Dec (DMB DT CJH). Skinflats: 2900 on 21 Jan, 3700 on 18 Feb, still 76 on 1 Jun & 5 on 30th; 2940 on 8 Dec (MVB GO).

RUFF *Philomachus pugnax (p)*
F   2 Skinflats 20 May & 1 on 23rd (AB GO). 1st of autumn 1 Kinneil 4 Aug, max 5 on 12 Sep, last 1 on 28th. 2 Skinflats 24 Aug, last 1 on 22 Sep (DT RS DAC GO).
C   8 Tullibody Inch 22 Sep (DMB).
Area Summary (half monthly)

May	Aug	Sep
0 2	1 4	7 12

JACK SNIPE *Lymnocryptes minimus (w)*
F   Kinneil: 1 on 11 Feb; 3 on 15 Dec & 4 on 26th. 2 Grangemouth 26 Oct & 1 on 8 Dec. (IW SH RS DT DMB).
C   1 Cambus Pools 21 Aug (an early date WRB).
S   1 Kinbuck 10 Nov (WRB)

SNIPE *Gallinago gallinago (B,W)*
     Probably under-recorded in breeding season but may have decreased (Ed).
F   36 Grangemouth 26 Oct & 26 on 8 Dec (DMB). 3 Kinneil 4 Aug & max only 12 on 1 Sep (DT AB). 8 Higgins Neuk 20 Nov (DF).
C   1 Upper Glendevon Res 15 Jun (CJH). 12 Cambus Pools 19 Aug (WRB).
S   8 drumming R.Balvaig (Balquhidder) 1 Apr (MT). 2 Killin Marshes 24 May (PWS). 15 Cambuskenneth 17 Nov & 26 on 15 Dec (AT). 10 on Forth at Drip Carse 18 Nov (RC). Autumn numbers elswhere not above 4.

WOODCOCK *Scolopax rusticola (B,W)*
     Under-recorded in breeding season (Ed).
F/S   Roding or in breeding season at: Dunmore, Torwood, Lecropt, Dunblane (3), R.Balvaig, L.Venachar, Kippen (GB AB GO AD SH MVB DAC).
F   1 in garden Grangemouth 20 Oct (GO). *Presumably a migrant! Ed.*

BLACK-TAILED GODWIT *Limosa limosa (W)*

F   Kinneil was the major site with Skinflats being significant only in early Mar, May and early Aug. Numbers varied around 30 in the first five months with many extra birds on 24 Apr (GO). After very few in June and early July, numbers built up to an autumn plateau of around 70 by late Aug, including 2 at Higgins Neuk on the 28th. Variation after this is probably due to the flock splitting whilst apparent absence in late Nov is surely due to lack of observation. (many contributors)

C   30 Cambus Pools 19 Aug (WRB) & 1 Tullibody Inch 18 Sep (CJH).

S   About 8 found dead under pylons in Glen Lochay in April (per RSPB). *A much larger flock must have been passing, presumably moving from the Forth/Tay area to the west coast and then Iceland. This sad event corresponds with the April increase noted at Skinflats, Ed.*

	Jan	Feb	Mar	Apr	May	Jun	Jul	Aug	Sep	Oct	Nov	Dec
Knnl	31 32	18 16	0 22	32	95 29 11	6 2	4 14	14 50	35 66	42 76	70 –	74 78
Sknf			3	16 5	15 20 19		1	15 3	6			
Area	32 32	18 19	16 27	32	110 49 30	6 2	4 15	29 85	35 73	42 76	70 –	74 78

BAR-TAILED GODWIT *Limosa lapponica (W)*

248 Forth Estuary 18 Feb & 223 on 8 Dec (DMB).

F   Kinneil: 300 on 7 Jan, 210 on 1 Feb & 10 on 9 Mar; 1st of autumn 2 on 7 Jul, 60 on 3 Nov, 150 on 29 Dec (AB CJH DT WRB). 5 Skinflats 4 Jun (AB).

C   1 Cambus 26 Sep (WRB).

WHIMBREL *Numenius phaeopus (p)*

F   2 ->NW Bo'ness 25 Apr, 3 Skinflats 7 May (RS). 1st of autumn, 1 Kinneil 9 Jul; exceptional numbers there in Aug: 28 on 24th - most arrived from N & left SE, 45 left W on 29th (DT). Last on 29 Sep (AB).

S   3 Bandeath 5 May (DMB). At least 2 in party of 8 *Numenius sp* ->NW Stirling 4 Sep (DT).

Area Summary (half monthly)

Apr	May	Jun	Jul	Aug	Sep
0 5	7 0	0 0	2 1	4 48	5 1

CURLEW *Numenius arquata (B,W)*

The March return & passage is clear in inland records (Ed). 574 Forth Estuary 18 Feb & 248 on 8 Dec (DMB).

F   Kinneil: 3 on 30 Jun, 225 on 7 Jul, 510 on 17 Aug (DT MVB). Skinflats: 302 on 21 Jan, 200 on 18 Feb, 36 on 2 Mar; 280 on 26 Oct, 100 on 21 Dec (AB AD MVB). 53 Higgins Neuk 23 Sep (DF).

C   39 R.Devon Dollar 23 Mar (RN). 4 AoT Devon WBS (CJH). 74 Cambus 17 Nov (KD).

S   4 Lecropt 10 Mar & 50 on 23rd (DT DAC). 2 AoT on Cromlix BBS, 3 AoT on Doune CBC (WRB NB). 11 Upper Glendevon Res 16 Jun (CJH). 1st departure from breeding sites, 1 ->SW Dunblane 24 Jun (MVB).

SPOTTED REDSHANK *Tringa erythropus* *(p)*
F   1 Skinflats 1 Mar to 18 Apr. At Kinneil from 16 Aug to 29 Dec (GO AD
       AB DT).
S   1 Carron Valley Res 21 Sep (GJB).
       Area Total

Mar	Apr	-	Aug	Sep	Oct	Nov	Dec
1 1	1 1	-	0 2	2 3	1 1	1 0	1 1

REDSHANK *Tringa totanus* *(B,W)*
       1465 Forth Estuary 21 Jan & 1839 on 8 Dec (DMB).
F   Skinflats: 570 on 21 Jan, 130 on 7 Mar; 110 on 14 Jun, 585 on 15 Sep,
       582 on 8 Dec. (AB MVB). Kinneil: 160 on 17 Jul & 350 on 21st , 400 on
       4 & 21 Sep (DT). 140 Higgins Neuk 23 Sep, 185 on 9 Dec (DF).
C   Pair bred Cambus (WRB). 3 on R.Devon 11 Mar (NB), 4 AoT Devon
       WBS (CJH).
S   4 Kippen Muir 27 Mar to 28 Jul (DAC). 2 on Forth at Gargunnock 10
       Mar (MT).

GREENSHANK *Tringa nebularia* *(p)*
F   1 -> N Bo'ness 22 May (RS). 1 Skinflats 20 May & regular to 29 Sep,
       max 5 on 23 Aug. 2 Kinneil 4 Aug, max 5 on 6 Sep, last on 17 Sep (GO
       AB DT RS). 1 juv on R.Carron at Larbert 7 to 10 Sep (MA).
C   1 Cambus Pools 21 Aug & 7 Sep (WRB CJH).
       Area Summary (half monthly)

May	Jun	Jul	Aug	Sep	Oct
0 2	1 2	1 1	3 10	10 6	0 0

*GREEN SANDPIPER *Tringa ochropus* *(p)*
F   2 Kinneil 10 Aug, 3 on 29th & 1 on 31st (GO RS DT). 1 Skinflats 22 &
       27 Aug & 2 on 30th (AB GO). 1 on R.Carron at Larbert 17 Oct (MA).

*WOOD SANDPIPER *Tringa glareola*
F   1 imm Skinflats 6 & 8 Aug (GO RS).

COMMON SANDPIPER *Tringa hypoleucos* *(B)*
       Spring return: 1 Barbush 18 Apr, 2 on Devon on 19th, 4 Cambus & 1
       Kinbuck on 20th, 3 Loch Arklet 3 May & widespread thereafter (WRB
       CJH MVB DAC).
F   Kinneil: 1st on 30 Jun, 7 on 21 Jul, 5 on 4 & 12 Aug, last on 4 Sep. 3 at
       Skinflats 11 Aug, last on 25th. (GO DT).
C   3 AoT on Devon WBS. 1st of autumn Tullibody Inch 7 Jul (CJH).
S   In summer at Doune CBC (1 AoT), L.Arklet, L.Katrine (W), L.Voil,
       Auchtoo (Balquhidder), Lake of Menteith, LRusky (NB DAC AD DT).
       1 Ashfield 15 Sep & 17 Nov (MW) - *last date very late Ed.*

Estuary autumn totals:	Jun	Jul	Aug	Sep
	0 1	2 10	8 6	2 0

TURNSTONE *Arenaria interpres* *(W)*
F   32 Blackness 27 Dec (AS).

*ARCTIC SKUA   Stercorarius parasiticus (p)
F   Grangemouth area: 12 on 11 Aug, 11 on 21 Sep - all flying upstream;
        Also 3 "probables" on 9 Sep & 1 on 29th (DT).

BLACK-HEADED GULL   Larus ridibundus   (B,W)
F   1st juv at Skinflats 29 Jun (AB).
C   4000 Tullibody Inch 23 Dec (CJH).
S   1200 on damp pasture Blairlogie 18 Feb (CJH). 80 at Ashfield colony 3
        Mar, most deserted; 2-3 pairs reared 4Y. 250 pairs reared 150 Y
        Hutchison Dam. 35 pairs reared 20 Y Hillhead Pond (WRB). 23 AoT
        Cambusmore on 8 Jun. Groups of 50 & 150 were hawking at Stirling 5
        Aug (CJH).

COMMON GULL   Larus canus   (B,W)
C   160 Upper Glendevon Res 16 Jun, 64 nests incubated, clutch sizes - 11
        c/3, 4 c/2, 3 c/1, date suggests relaying of robbed nests (CJH).
S   500 Buchlyvie 18 Feb & 600 on 30 Oct; 696 Gargunnock 10 Mar (DAC
        MT). 27 AoT Cambusmore GP 8 Jun (CJH). 1 nest L.Arklet, 12 nests
        L.Watston 11 May, 2 AoT Barbush (WRB). 1 AoT Hillhead Pond (NB).
        60, some nests, Breachlaich Res (Killin) 9 Jun (PWS).

LESSER BLACK-BACKED GULL   Larus fuscus (b,S)0
        Few mid-winter records, as usual; increasing nest attempts on roofs; more
        stayed late into autumn.
F   1 Skinflats 6 Jan, 1 on 25 Feb & 11 on 2 Mar, 1 Kinneil 26 Feb (GO CJH).
        Pair bred on roof Grangemouth (DMB WRB). 29 Skinflats 1 Aug (AB).
        34 Little Denny Res 16 Sep, 72 L.Ellrig 11 Oct (NB).
C   38 around Menstrie whisky bond roofs 3 Jun, 10 apparently on nests
        on 6th. 15 on Cambus bond roofs 3 Jun. 21 Tullibody Inch 18 Sep, 2 on
        14 Dec (CJH BRT).
S   1 L.Coulter 5 Jan (NB); 1 Stirling 4 Dec & 1 Killin on 27th (DT PWS). 1
        Stirling 16 Feb & 2 Lake of Menteith 2 Mar (DT). 2 AoT Cambusmore
        GP 12 Jun (PWS). 25(20J) Vale of Coustry 5 Sep, 27 Thornhill 10 Oct
        (NB CJH).

HERRING GULL   Larus argentatus (b?,S,W)
F   6000 Kinneil 7 Jan & 5000 on 18th; 4500 on 28 Dec (CJH).
C   4 (1 apparently on nest) Menstrie bond roofs 7 Jun (CJH).
S   1100 on Fallin tip 29 Jul. Roosting Cambus-Tullibody Inch: 4500 on 4
        Sep & 1470 on 18th, 2400 on 23 Dec (CJH)

*GLAUCOUS GULL   Larus hyperboreus
F   1(1st winter) Kinneil 11 Feb, 1 Grangemouth on 18th (IW SH RS
        MVB).

GREAT BLACK-BACKED GULL   Larus marinus (S,W)
        Highly under-reported (Ed).
F   30 Kinneil 28 Dec (CJH).
C   49 Tullibody Inch 18 Sep & 43 on 26 Nov (CJH).
S   27 L.Coulter 5 Jan - high count for inland (NB).

KITTIWAKE *Rissa tridactyla (P,w)*
F   Kinneil: 1 on 6 & 7 Jan (GO AB). 90 on 28 Apr landed, returned high
      to E. 40 Ad ->W on 22 Jun, 250 on 26 Jul, 30 ->E 20 Sep (DT). Skinflats:
      2 dead Imm 13 Apr (DT), 150 left high to NE on 6 Jun (GO). *(These
      summer movements seem very odd, Ed).*

SANDWICH TERN *Sterna sandvicensis (P)*
F   1st Grangemouth 28 Apr (DT).10 Bo'ness 15 Sep (CJH). 28 Kinneil 3
      Sep & 61 on 22nd, last 12 on 28th (GO DMB).
C   15 Cambus 7 Sep (CJH).
S   3 Carron Valley Res 6 Aug (RKP).

COMMON TERN *Sterna hirundo (B)*
F   lst, 3 Skinflats 27 Apr, 21 Kinneil & 15 Grangemouth on 28th (GO DT).
      At Grangemouth colony on 9 Jun there were 102 pairs, at least 25Y on
      19 Jul (DMB WRB).
C   4 Cambus on 4 May &12 on 12th (DMB CJH).
S   1 Airthrey 12 Apr (DMB).

*ARCTIC TERN *Sterna paradisaea*
F   1 Skinflats 5 Jun (GO).

*BLACK TERN *Chlidonias niger*
F   1 (Juv) Higgins Neuk 4 Aug (MA), similar bird at Kinneil 10 Aug &
      Skinflats on 20th (RS GO).

GUILLEMOT *Uria aalge (W)*
F   A few on the Forth from Kinneil to Alloa Jan & Feb, & 1 at Stirling 25
      Dec (GO AB MVB BRT JGH). Also 3 Grangemouth 12 Jul & 15
      Skinflats 19 Sep; 56 dead on tideline at Skinflats 13 Apr probably relate
      to the inland influx in late Jan (DT GO).
C   10 Tullibody Inch 28 Jan (DMB).
S   1 flying over Drip Camp 27 Jan (SS), on 28th 2 ->W & 1->E over
      Lecropt, +1 injured, also 2+3+3 -> W over Blairdrummond carse at
      Arnieve (DT CJH).

*RAZORBILL *Alca torda (w)*
F   1 Kinneil 17 Mar (GO). 4 dead on tideline Skinflats 13 Apr (DT).

*PUFFIN
F   65 Grangemouth 12 Jul, in parties flying about, no juvs seen (DT).
      *(Apparently 1st record since 1970, are we missing birds from Isle of May that
      come up Firth in midsummer to feed? Ed).*

ROCK DOVE / FERAL PIGEON *Columba livia (B,W)*
S   152 Dunblane 6 Jan (WRB).

STOCK DOVE *Columba oenas (B,W)*
      Widespread in small numbers, surely much overlooked (Ed)
F   21 Kinneil 2 Jun (DT). In Jun & Sep by R.Carron at Larbert (MA).
C   Probably 1 AoT on Devon WBS (CJH).

S   6 BoA 3 Feb; 1 singing Aberfoyle 31 May was at W edge of range
       (WRB).

WOODPIGEON Columba palumba (B,W)
       Greatly underreported, have the really large flocks of the past disappeared ?
C   29 Dollar 28 Dec (BRT). Max 32 on Devon WBS 3 Apr (CJH). The most
       reported from Clacks ! Ed
S   7 AoT on Doune CBC (NB). 200 Lecropt 5 Jan (IW). 300 Park of Keir 23
       Feb & 400 on 22 Mar, feeding on, probably, young oilseed rape (NB).

COLLARED DOVE Streptopelia decaocto (B,W)
       Under-reported, but scarce away from suburbs and large farms (Ed)
F   26 Polmont 26 Feb (JW). Vagrant to Skinflats, 1 on 4 & 12 May (GO).
C   45 Cambus, Orchard Fm, 26 Nov (CJH).
S   1 pair on Doune CBC (NB). 3 Killin 24 May, 2 in Sep & Dec (PWS). 2
       mating BoA 7 Nov (KD) - if breeding season so long, why not larger flocks?
       Ed.

CUCKOO Cuculus canorus (B)
       1st records at Torwood 27 Apr & Thornhill on 28th, Braeval on 1 May,
       Menteith Hills on 4th & Balquhidder on 6th (AB SS WRB DT AD).
       Summer records at Cocksburn (BoA), L.Katrine (juv fed by pipits) (AT
       DAC).
       Last records 2 Ad Ben Gullipen 12 Aug & a Juv on Braes of Doune on
       27th (DJC WRB).

*BARN OWL Tyto alba (b,w)
F   1 found dead Kinneil 4 Mar (GO). 2 around mine shaft at Denny in
       Jul (C.Perkins).
S   Up to 2 seen Gargunnock-Kippen Jan, Mar, Oct to Dec (HK DR). 1 at
       Thornhill, Lecropt & Stirling in Jan-Feb (SS JW WRB). Found dead in
       Dec at Killin & L.Watston (PWS CJH).

TAWNY OWL Strix aluco (B,W)
F   Reported Larbert Hospital, Carronvale, Torwood (JW JMr GO).
C   Reported Gartmorn, Alva (AT PMA).
S   Reported 3 sites BoA, Doune Ponds, Dunblane, Stirling, Plean CP,
       Lake of Menteith (AT KD WRB DT).

*LONG-EARED OWL Asio otus (b,w)
F   4Y Skinflats, only 3 seen as Juvs (AB GO RS).
C   Pair with 3Y Cambus in Jun (SH WRB).
S   1 Sheriffmuir 7 & 11 May; 1 Carron Valley Res 24 May (SH GO).

SHORT-EARED OWL Asio flammeus (b,W)
F   Kinneil: 1 from 20 Jan to 28 Apr, 2 on 2 Mar; 2 Skinflats 1 Mar & 1 on
       30th (GO DT RS IW CJH AB).
C   1 Glenquey 26 Jun & 9 Nov (PMA RN). 1 Cambus 12 Dec (WRB).
S   1 Cringate Muir 24 May (GO). 1 Invertrossachs 16 Aug (DOE). 1
       Arivurichardich 9 Aug (DJC). 2 Lecropt 23 Mar & 1 to 28 Apr (DAC HK

CJH). 1 Blairdrummond Carse 9 Jan to 19 Feb, 2 on 17 Jan (CJH). 1 Thornhill Carse 15 Nov to 27 Dec (DR).

SWIFT *Apus apus (B)*
    1st records: BoA on 1 May, Airthrey on 2nd, Callendar, Grangemouth & Plean on 7th (CJH DMB DJC DT). Last records in August: Dunblane on 12th, BoA on 13th, Kippen on 16th, Stirling on 18th (WRB CJH HK DT).
F   80 Skinflats 19 Jul (WRB).
S   Arrival at Killin 24 May (PWS). 2 boxes occupied Kippen, young fed to16 Aug but all absent next day (HK). Max 65 BoA 25 Jul & 70 on 6 Aug (CJH). 60 Stirling 22 Jul but only 20 Dunblane on 19th (WRB).

*KINGFISHER *Alcedo atthis (b,w)*
F   1 Carronshore 20 Sep to 19 Nov; 1 Kinneil 3 to 11 Feb, 2 Oct & 8 Nov; 1 on Avon at Grangemouth 4 Aug (AB CJH RS IW SH KD DT DT). 1 Linlithgow Bridge 17 Nov (AS). 2 on Carron at Larbert all year, burrow seen & 3J in late summer (MA JMr). 2 on Carron at Bonnybridge all year (MA).
C   2 on Devon at Tillicoultry 18 Jan to 23 Mar (RN). 1 on Devon WBS 25 May (CJH). 1 Cambus 10 Jun (SH).
S   On R.Allan: at BoA 2 on 31 Mar & 1 or 2 from 15 Jul to 31 Dec (CJH AT); at Dunblane-Ashfield-Kinbuck 1 or 2 from 14 Jun to 28 Dec (WGS MW SHs WRB KD). 1 Airthrey 10 Feb (PMA). 1 Callendar 8 Dec (DJC).

GREEN WOODPECKER *Picus viridis (B,W)*
F   1 Torwood 7 Apr (AB).
C   Alva in Jul & Oct, Dollar Jun to Dec (PMA RN).
S   Seen through year at Plean CP, 3 on 4 Mar, nest building on 29 Apr (HMR AB). 1 Blairlogie 22 Jun (DAC). Calling Mine Wood Feb, Jul, Dec (WRB AT). At Carron Valley Res only in summer (GJB). In spring/summer reported from: Kippen, Dunblane, 2 sites L.Ard Forest, Aberfoyle, L.Chon, Strathyre, Balquhidder, Killin (MT WRB IW RAB RY).

GREAT SPOTTED WOODPECKER *Dendrocopus major (B,W)*
    Greatly under reported from S & SWP
F   Bred Drumore, drumming from 18 Feb (GB). Pair feeding Juv by R.Carron at Larbert Jun & Jul, M on 14 Dec (MA). Through year at Polmont, Haining & Parkhill woods (JW).
C   Summer records at Alva, Dollar (PMA RN).
S   At Plean CP Apr - Jul (HMR). Jan -Jul at Mine Wood & Kippenrait Glen, juvs seen in Apr & Jul (AT). Noted in Apr at Buchlyvie & in Dec at Gargunnock & L.Venachar (DAC).

SKYLARK *Alauda arvensis (B,W)*
    Only 10 notes sent in, Ed
F   Singing Carronshore 3 Mar (AB). 30 ->SE Kinneil 13 Oct (DT). 52 in stubble Larbert 15 Dec (MA).

C   Widespread along Devon at Alva 25 Feb, 11 AoT on WBS (CJH).
S   3.6 AoT per sq km on Doune CBC, 35 % of 1995 (NB). 65 Lecropt 5 Jan,
     10 singing there on 10 Mar (IW DT). 25 ->SW Kippen Muir 5 Oct, 16
     ->SW Stronend on 21st (DT CJH).

SAND MARTIN *Riparia riparia (B)*
     1st records: 1 Lake of Menteith 30 Mar, Barbush on 5 Apr, Tullibody
     Inch on 6th, Airthrey on 9th, Stirling on 10th; 130 Airthrey on 18th &
     75 L.Dochart on 21st (DT WRB CJH DMB IW MVB WRB). Last 200
     Carronshore on 7 Sep (AB).
F   80 Skinflats 26 Jul (GO).
C   Devon WBS colony abandoned (CJH).
S   Nest counts: 270 Cambusmore GP in early Jun (DJC CJH).

SWALLOW *Hirundo rustica (B)*
     1st records: Airthrey 12 Apr, Kinneil, R.Avon & Bonnybridge on 13th,
     Crianlarich on 15th; widespread by 17th to 21st. Last in Oct;
     Gargunnock on 1st, 15 Airthrey on 2nd, 1 ->WSW Stronend on 21st
     (DMB MVB AB GO GB DT DAC CJH).
F   75 -> SE Skinflats 22 Sep (DT).
C   200 at dusk around Tullibody Inch on 8 Sep (CJH).
S   7.2 AoT per sq km on Doune CBC, 67 % of 1995 (NB). 1500 at roost
     Doune Ponds 15 Sep (DOE).

HOUSE MARTIN *Delichon urbica (B)*
     1st records: Airthrey 18 Apr; next reported were 2 Balquhidder on 6
     May & arrived Killin 24 May (MVB DMB DT PWS). Absent from
     Buchlyvie after 19 Sep, more usual last dates were in Oct: 10 Airthey
     on 2nd, 20 Dunblane on 4th, 1 Stirling on 7th (DAC WRB DT).
S   19.2 nests per sq Km on Doune CBC, 80 % of 1995 (NB). 5 nests
     Ashfield. 6 nests Ledcreich (L.Voil). 150 Ashfield 27 Aug & 120
     Dunblane 10 Sep, far more than local population (WRB MVB).

TREE PIPIT *Anthus trivialis (B)*
     1st records: 1 L.Ard 24 April, Braeval 1 May & 2 Rhuveag on 6th
     (WRB).

MEADOW PIPIT *Anthus pratensis (B,W)*
F   150 Skinflats 22 Sep (DT).
C   On lower Devon to 4 May (CJH).
S   Abundant in Glen Lochay 7 Apr (CJH). Visible movements in Oct: 65
     ->SW Kippen Muir on 5th (DT), small groups to S & SW at Callander
     on 2nd, Bat a' Charcel (Drymen road) on 10th, Stronend & Myot Hill
     on 21st (CJH).

*ROCK PIPIT *Anthus petrosus (w)*
F   1 Blackness on 27 Dec (CJH).

*YELLOW WAGTAIL *Motacilla flava*
     F Skinflats 26 Apr & pair on 2 & 3 May (GO AB). F Cambus Pools 5
     May (CJH).

GREY WAGTAIL *Motacilla cinerea (B,w)*
Winter records (Jan-Feb, Nov-Dec): 1 Larbert 17 Feb, 1 BoA 1 to 28 Nov, Tillicoultry 20 Nov, 1 Alva 2 Dec, 1 Higgins Neuk 9 Dec, 1 Cambuskenneth 15 Dec. Records suggesting spring return at Polmont 3 Mar & Plean CP on 4th, BoA on 16th, then L.Voil, Ashfield, Alva & Larbert 27 to 31 Mar (GO AT JGL PMA DF JW HMR DAC WRB AS).
S   Many sites unoccupied this spring (HR). Summer records at Buchlyvie, Deanston, 2 sites Glen Lochay (DAC RY). 1 still at l.Voil 27 Sep (NB).

PIED WAGTAIL *Motacilla alba (B, w)*
F   200 at roost BP Grangemouth 18 Mar (SH). Skinflats: 13 on 26 Apr & 25 on 2 May (GO). White Wagtails *M.a.alba*: 2 Kinneil 28 Apr, 2 Skinflats 2 May &1 on 3rd (GO AB).
C   4 AoT on Devon CBS. 80 Cambus 4 Sep (CJH).
S   26 Buchlyvie 3 Apr (DAC). 60 at roost Stirling 16 Sep (DT).

WAXWING *Bombycilla garrulus*
F   30 Denny 5 Feb (RSPB). Falkirk: 24 on 26 Jan, max 36 on 11 Feb, last 20 on 16 Feb (B.Waddell, SH JW). 2 Grangemouth 23 Feb (GO). 11 Bo'ness 5 Mar, 18 on 29th & 1 on 2 Apr (AS RS). Autumn records from Falkirk area: 17 on 8 Dec to 11 on 31st at Polmont (JW), 3 Camelon on 13 Dec & 5 on 12th (MA).
C   20 Dollar 15 Jan, 12 from 22 Jan to 25 Feb. 12 on 23 Nov (AT SH).
S   30 Stirling 26 Jan, max 70 on 31st, 44 on 2 Feb, last 3 on 27 Mar (DT IW) - *possibly two large groups, Ed.*
6 Killin 20 Nov (PWS). 65 Stirling on 19 Nov, 80 on 21st, 1 on 19 Dec (IW GO WRB).

DIPPER *Cinclus cinclus (B,W)*
Greatly underrecorded.
F   2, song, R.Carron at Larbert on 17 Feb (GO).
S   2 pairs on Doune CBC (NB). Average site occupancy in Trossachs/Kippen (HR).

WREN *Troglodytes troglodytes (B,W)*
Under-recorded (Ed). NB the woodland density is almost 25 times greater than the farmland.
C   13 AoT on 5 km of lower Devon, much as 1995 (CJH).
S   16 M territories in 14 Ha of Mine Wood, 73 % of 1995 though only 14 % survival of that year's territory holders - ie considerable influx of new Ms (M.Evans). 4.8 AoT per sq Km Doune CBC (only 38 % of 1995, NB).

HEDGE SPARROW *Accentor modularis (B,W)*
Under-recorded (Ed).
C   6 AoT on 5 Km of lower Devon, as 1995 (CJH).
S   7.2 pair per sq km on Doune CBC (75 % of 1995) (NB). 3 fed on sunflower seeds at BoA on 8 Dec (KD).

ROBIN   *Erithacus rubecula   (B,W)*
   Under-recorded (Ed)
F   1 fed from hand during deep snow in Dunmore Wood 25 Dec (GB).
C   2 AoT on 5 km of lower Devon (5 in 1995) (CJH).
S   3.6 pairs per sq km on Doune CBC (60% of 1995). This year only 10th
   commonest species through year in Dunblane garden (NB).

*BLACK REDSTART   *Phoenicurus ochrurus*
S   1, F or imm, on Thornhill Carse 26 Oct & 1 Nov (DR). *(only two previous*
   records : one shot at Higgins Neuk on 10 Nov 1875 & one at Kinneil on 23
   Jan 1983, Ed).

REDSTART   *Phoenicurus phoenicurus (B)*
   1st records L.Ard on 24 Apr, Achray Water & Bo'ness on 28th, Braeval
   on 1 May, Balquhidder on 6th & Menteith Hills on 8th. In autumn M
   Ashfield 25 Jul & 1 Skinflats 11 Aug were migrants, last at Buchlyvie
   on 23 Aug & Braes of Doune on 27th (WRB DAC RS DT IW).
S   38 nest attempts at Trossachs colony, 32 successful (HR). F with Juv
   Buchlyvie 10 Aug was 1st record in 4 years *(suggests local breeding, Ed)*
   (DAC).

WHINCHAT   *Saxicola rubetra (B)*
   Under-recorded as breeding   (Ed).
   1st records: 3 L.Ard Forest & 1 Skinflats on 2 May, 1 Kippen Muir on
   5th, Doune CBC & 3 Menteith Hills on 8th. Autumn migrants at
   Ashfield 22 Jul, Kinneil 24 Aug, Cambus 13 Aug (WRB AB DAC NB
   DT).
S   Several pairs Monachyle Glen 12 May (WRB). Family parties
   Glengyle-L.Katrine on 22 Jun (DAC).

*STONECHAT   *Saxicola torquata (b,w)*
   Distinct signs of population decrease , presumably related to severe winter
   (Ed).
S   1 Doune Ponds 21 Mar (AD). M in song Monachyle Glen 12 May, 1
   Hutchison Ptn 2 Jul & 2 on 12 Oct. Pair bred L.Arklet, alarm calls on
   18 Jul (WRB).

WHEATEAR   *Oenanthe oenanthe (B)*
   Under-recorded as breeding in C, S (Ed).
   1st records: 1 L.Arklet & Skinflats 4 Apr, Cringate Muir on 6th, Glen
   Lochay & Kinneil on 7th, Doune on 11th (IW GO DT CJH NB). Arrival
   (5) at Arnprior on 21 Apr. 5 on arable at Doune CBC on 7 May were
   migrants & there were a few at Alva, Ashfield & on estuary 13 Apr to
   10 May. Autumn migrants at Ashfield, Kinneil & Skinflats 13 to 25
   Aug, last at Dumyat on 31 Aug & Buchlyvie 4 Sep (DAC NB DT CJH
   AB GO WRB).
C   Several Juv below Lower Glendevon Res 16 Jun (CJH).
S   12 pairs Inverlochlarig 12 May (DOE). 2 pairs Breachlaich Quarry
   (Killin) 9 Jun (PWS). Several with young Glengyle-L.Katrine on 22 Jun
   (DAC).

*RING OUSEL *Turdus torquatus (b)*
S   Song at Monachyle Glen 29 Mar to 12 May (DAC AD WRB). Pair +
2M Rhuveag 6 May (DT). 6 Cam Chreag (Glen Lochay) 14 Jul & 1 at
2nd site 3 Aug (RY).

BLACKBIRD *Turdus merula (B,W)*
F   4 AoT Dunmore Wood (GB).
C   9 AoT on 5 Km of lower Devon, much as 1995 (CJH).
S   7th commonest garden species Dunblane. 18 pairs per sq km on
Doune CBC, much as 1995 (NB). 12 feeding on apples BoA 27 Dec
(KD).

FIELDFARE *Turdus pilaris (W)*
April departure included 200 Arnprior on 8th, 24 Dunmore on 15th &
103 -> NE Doune on 11th (DAC GB NB).
1st of autumn hundreds at Killin 15 &16 Oct, then 107->SE Dunblane
on 18th; parties widespread on 19th with 50 -> SW at Alva, 50->W at
Cambus & 300 ->SW at Lecropt; 75->WSW Stronend on 21st & many
large parties on 26th with 460->SW Kennetpans, 350 Cambus, 450
Buchlyvie & 200 Gartmore. Large parties widespread to 17 Nov, but
in Dec only 150 Lecropt on 1st & 200 Skinflats on 22nd (PWS CJH
PMA WRB DT DAC AT MVB).
F   150 Shieldhill 21 Jan (MA).
S   200 Gartmore Jan 11, 300 Sheriffmuir on 15th & 234 Port of Menteith
on 16th. Only large flock in Feb was 124 Drumloist on 22nd (CJH NB).
One bird in a flock of 60 at Buchlyvie on 6 Jan had pure white face
patches, like a Great Tit (DAC). *Redwings also notorious for strange
plumage variations (Ed).*

SONG THRUSH *Turdus philomelos (B,W)*
Under-recorded as breeding (Ed). Few in mid-winter - 1 BoA 26 Dec
(though 4 fighting at a birdbath on 22 Nov); in Feb birds at
Blairdrummond Carse on 11th, Buchlyvie on 21st & Plean CP on 28th
suggest return in early spring (AT KD CJH DAC HMR).
F   4 AoT Dunmore Wood (GB).
C   1 AoT in 5 km lower Devon, 3 in 1995 (CJH).
S   1 pair on Doune CBC (NB).

REDWING *Turdus iliacus (W)*
1st of autumn 9 at Airthrey on 9 Oct, then none till 15th &16th with
many hundreds at Killin. On the 18th there were 220 Hill of Rew &
500->ESE at BoA; on 19th 100->SW Alva, 400->W Cambus, 650->SW
Lecropt, 200 Stirling & 300 Buchlyvie; on 20th 200 left E in Strathallan
& 55 flew S in Strathyre, on 21st 115 ->S Myothill & 190->WSW
Stronend. Large parties were widespread on 26th but much scarcer
through November and December (MVB PWS CJH PMA WRB DT
DAC)
S   Flocks of 50 in Jan & Feb; 95 BoA 22 Mar, last 3 Stronachlachar on

4 Apr & 100 Kippen on 7th (WRB AT DAC). On 29 Dec 13 foraged in leaves in garden at BoA (KD).

MISTLE THRUSH   *Turdus viscivorus   (B,W)*
   Under-recorded, the 1st large flocks for some years (Ed)
S   1 AoT Plean CP (HMR). Only seen twice in 78 hr on Doune CBC (NB) (None seen in 24 hr on Devon WBS). 24 Airthrey 26 Aug, 12-> SW Ashfield 24 Sep; 7 Braeleny 2 Oct & 40 Buchlyvie on 6th, 5 -> WSW Stronend 21 Oct (MVB WRB CJH DAC).

*GRASSHOPPER WARBLER   *Locustella naevia (b)*
      Seems to have become scarce in last few years (Ed)
F   1 Skinflats 26 Apr to 27 Jul (AB GO RS). 1 singing Carronshore 29 Apr to10 Jun (AB). 1 singing Kinneil 7 Jul (DT).
C   1 AoT Devon WBS from 15 May (CJH). Song at Cambus Pool 18 May & 21 Jun, 2 giving alarm calls 16 & 19 Aug, late bird on 16 Sep (CJH WRB).
S   1 Flanders Moss (SWT) 8 Aug & 1 at 2nd site 13 Jun (TJ).

SEDGE WARBLER   *Acrocephalus schoenobaenus (B)*
      Under-recorded as breeder (Ed)
F   1 Skinflats 23 Apr, 4 on 28th. 2 Kinneil on 28 Apr (GO DT)
C   3 AoT Cambus from 18 May, juvs seen on 17 Aug, last 7 on 20 Aug (CJH DAC WRB). 49 AoT on Devon WBS, none on 19 Apr but 25 % arrived by 4 May, still 20 % in song 16 Jul (CJH).
S   5 Doune Ponds 21 Apr (AD). At L.Watson & Lake of Menteith on 11 May (WRB SH). 1 AoT Doune CBC - not seen until 13 Jun (NB). Last 2 Ashfield 29 Aug (WRB).

WHITETHROAT   *Sylvia communis (B)*
      1st records: Larbert 22 Apr, Skinflats on 23rd; Dunmore on 2 May, Doune on 7th, at Menteith Hills & 6 Buchlyvie on 8 May. Last at Gartmorn on 24 Aug & Ashfield on 29th (JMr GO GB NB WRB DAC).
C   9 AoT on Devon WBS (as 1995), none on 4 May but 4 by 15th (CJH).
SWP   4.8 pairs per sq km Doune CBC, 36 % of 1995 (NB).

GARDEN WARBLER   *Sylvia borin (B)*
      1st records in May: Lake of Menteith on 11th, R.Devon on 15th, Doune Ponds on 19th (SH CJH WRB).
C   4 AoT Devon WBS, last bird arrived between 2 &12 Jun (CJH).
S   3 to 5 AoT Buchlyvie in Jun (DAC).

BLACKCAP   *Sylvia atricapilla (B)*
      Under-recorded as breeder (Ed)
      Winter records: Pair Alva 14 Jan, 1 Dollar Jan-Feb, F BoA 1 Jan to 20 Feb (ate honeysuckle berries) + M 16 Jan to 3 Mar (F from 23 Mar possibly early arrival); 1 Stirling 31 Jan & M+F 4 to 11 Feb, 2 at birdbath BoA 22 & 23 Nov, M+F Alva 7 to 27 Dec ate nuts, fat & mash potato (PMA SH CJH DMB AHH KD)
C   F + juvs Gartmorn 6 Jul (DAC).

F   Pairs at Falkirk on 10 Mar &, 2nd site, on 12 May (JW). Late bird in song at Skinflats 28 Sep (AB).

S   2 M Lake of Menteith 5 May (DAC). 3 singing Stirling castle 13 May (WRB). 1 Plean CP 12 May & pair 17 Jun (AB HMR).

WOOD WARBLER *Phylloscopus sibilatrix (B)*

S   1 Aberfoyle 30 Apr, 2 in song Kilmahog 3 May & Balquhidder on 11th (DOE RJ SH). At L.Chon in Jun (WRB).

CHIFFCHAFF *Phylloscopus collybita (B)*

         1st records: Lake of Menteith 2 Apr, Polmont & BoA on 4th, Dunmore on 5th, Dunblane on 8th, Callendar Park on 9th (DT MVB JW GB). 1st local sightings at Buchlyvie on 21 Apr & Doune CBC on 25th (DAC NB). Last Avon Aqueduct on 14 Sep & Gartmorn on 15th Sep (JW AT).

S   1 Plean CP 3 May (AB). 1 Stirling 11 Dec (J Mallett).

WILLOW WARBLER *Phylloscopus trochilus (B)*

         1st records: Polmont 8 Apr, Buchlyvie & Doune Ponds on 13th, Dunblane on 17th; Airthrey, Plean CP (8), Skinflats & Carronshore on 18th; Devon WBS (4) on 19th - all in by 4 May (JW DAC WRB MVB DT GO AB). Last, singles at Gartmore 15 Sep & Cambus on 16th (DAC WRB).

C   12 AoT on 5km of lower Devon, much as 1995 (CJH).

S   8.4 pairs per sq km on Doune CBC, 133 % of 1995 (NB). 7 on Cromlix BBS square in May (WRB).

GOLDCREST *Regulus regulus (B,W)*

         Greatly under-recorded (Ed)

C   1 AoT on Devon WBS - in only evergreen patch, Lawsons Cypresses (CJH).

S   3 spring sites near Buchlyvie, 1 Blairlogie; 6 L.Venachar 29 Dec (DAC).

SPOTTED FLYCATCHER *Muscicapa striata (B)*

         Under-recorded (Ed)

         1st records: in May, Falkirk on 12th, Stirling on 13th, Alva on 25th, BoA on 26th; 1st noted Buchlyvie on 7 Jun & Dollar on 10th (JW WRB PMA DMB DAC RN). Last, 1 Skinflats 25 Aug (DT).

S   In summer at least 4 sites around Buchlyvie, also Culcreuch, Drip Carse, L.Chon, Brig o'Turk, Killin (DAC PWS).

PIED FLYCATCHER *Ficedula hypoleuca (b)*

         1st records: M Achray Water 28 Apr, Doon Hill on 2 May, Larbert on 5th, Balquhidder (Rhuveag, 4) on 6th (DAC WRB MA DT).

C   M in song Alva 24 May (PMA).

S   65 nest attempts at Trossachs colony, 60 successful (HR). Pair nested at Forest Park visitor centre (WRB). Pair Pass of Leny 30 Jun & Brig o'Turk 18 Aug (DAC). M in song L.Tay (Ardeonaig) 19 May, F at nestbox on 23rd (PWS).

LONG-TAILED TIT   *Aegithalos caudatus   (B,W)*
F   3 broods totalling 30 Y Dunmore Wood (GB). 10 Howierig Wood (Falkirk) 13 Jan & 15 on 19 Nov (MA). 6 Skinflats 18 Feb (AB). 8 Bo'ness 5 Mar (AS).
S   6 Plean CP 19 May & 10 on 29 Nov (HMR AB). 15 Mine Wood 30 Nov (AT). 20 Daldorn 15 Dec (BWB). 12 Lecropt 21 Jan (IW). 14 L.Watston 21 Dec (CJH). 21 on Doune CBC 16 Jun. Fed at nut/seed feeders at Dunblane 6 Feb & BoA on 10 Nov (NB KD).

COAL TIT   *Parus ater   (B,W)*
        Greatly under-recorded (Ed)
S   7 fed at seed feeder BoA on 10 Nov (KD). Still 10th commonest species in Dunblane garden, mainly before mid-June & after mid November (NB).

BLUE TIT   *Parus caeruleus   (B,W)*
        Under-recorded (Ed)
C   10 in Alva garden Jan to Mar (PMA). 4 AoT on 5 Km of lower Devon, 10 in 1995 (CJH).
S   12 pair per sq km on Doune CBC, 2.5 x 1995 (NB). 11 fed at seed feeder BoA on 10 Nov (KD).

GREAT TIT   *Parus major   (B,W)*
        Under-recorded (Ed)
F   4 AoT Dunmore Wood (GB). 4Y fledged Larbert 9 Jun (MA).
C   2 AoT on 5 km of lower Devon (CJH).
S   8.4 pairs per sq km on Doune CBC, 3.5 times 1995 (NB).

TREECREEPER   *Certhia familiaris (B,W)*
        Under-recorded (Ed)
S   Recorded from Plean CP, Gargunnock, Arnprior, Lake of Menteith, Aberfoyle, Brig o'Turk, L.Venachar (AB DAC).

JAY   *Garrulus glandarius (B,W)*
        Under-recorded as breeder in SWP (Ed)
F   Recorded at Wallacebank Wood in Mar, Callendar CP & Larbert Hospital in Apr, Haining Wood in Oct, Kinneil in Dec, Torwood through year (AS JW AB).
C   Recorded Alva in Jun & Sep,   Gartmorn in Sep, Dollar in Feb, Glenquey in Jun (PMA RN).
S   Spring/summer records from Buchlyvie, Aberfoyle, Blackwater Marshes, Carron Valley Res, Kippenrait Glen, Stirling; in Autumn from the western of these localities, plus Doune & L.Watston; acorn collecting in Oct (DAC NB RJ CJH).

MAGPIE   *Pica pica (B,W)*
        Its abundance around Stirling is not necessarily noted in the west and east of the area (Ed).
F   2 Dunmore through year (GB).
C   4 AoT on 5 km of lower Devon (CJH).

S   40 Airthrey 28 Feb, 72 at roost on 13th. 28 Lecropt 28 Dec (DMB MVB).
        Max 4 Plean CP Feb-Mar (HMR). 1 AoT (first) on Doune CBC, 1 in
        Dunblane garden May & Jun (NB). 2 Kippen Muir 1 Feb, 1 Buchlyvie
        31 Mar (1st record), also in Jul & Oct. Aberfoyle: 2 Malling 17 Sep & 1
        Balleich (4 km west) 21 Dec, both unusual records (DAC NB).

JACKDAW *Corvus monedula (B,W)*
         Greatly under-recorded (Ed)
C   70 Tullibody Inch 26 Nov (CJH).
S   Regular in Dunblane garden, max 15. 3.6 pair per sq km on Doune
        CBC, as 1995 (NB).

ROOK *Corvus frugilegus (B,W)*
        Rookery counts: BoA(N), 30 in decid, 163 in pines. BoA(S) 168; Witches Craig
        59; Myretoun 67. Total 487 (430 in 1995, increase in BoA N); also a new
        rookery: 35 at Menstrie nursery, close to Myretoun (CJH). 174
        Balquhidderock Wood (DT). 16 N.Doll (Dunmore) (GB).
C   An isolated pair nested at Alva, as 1995 (PMA). 60 in upper Alva Glen
        29 Feb - odd date for a hill flock (CJH).
S   1700 in stubble, Kippen 22 Nov (NB). 500 in a.m gathering Buchlyvie
        20 Feb, also 600 similarly on 31 Oct & 1 Nov (DAC).

CARRION CROW *Corvus corone (B,W)*
F   96 Kinneil 6 Jan & 225 on 27 May (GO).
C   Cambus roost, 125 on 6 Jan (CJH).
S   60 Dunblane 27 Nov. 7.2 AoT per km sq at Doune CBC (twice 1995)
        (NB). Hoodies: 1 Lake of Menteith 28 Mar & 1 (hybrid) Buchlyvie 22
        Nov were outside usual breeding range (DT NB). Summer records
        from Monachyle Glen & Glen Buckie were on E edge of main range
        (AT DAC).

RAVEN *Corvus corax (B,W)*
C   1 territory checked, unoccupied (PSA). However, birds seen in area in
        Mar (DMB DAC)
S   22 territories checked, 17 pairs, 8 successful pairs raised at least 16Y
        (PSA). Outwith of immediate breeding areas: 1 Cringate Muir 7 May
        (GO), 7 ->W Kippen 4 Mar (MT), 1 over Buchlyvie 31 Mar & 2
        Blackwater Marshes 18 Aug (DAC). 2 L.Laggan 6 Sep & 3 North Third
        Res 5 Oct (NB DT).

STARLING *Sturnus vulgaris (B,W)*
F   8 pairs bred N.Doll (Dunmore) (GB). Post breeding arrival at Skinflats,
        60 on 14 Jun (AB).
C   Tullibody Inch roost flight: 50 on 7 Jul (CJH). 400 Cambus 16 Aug
        (WRB).
S   15.6 pairs per sq km on Doune CBC, 130 % of 1995; fledglings from 4
        Jun - 12 days later than 1995; flock of 250 nearby as late as 11 Apr. 2nd
        commonest species in Dunblane garden, max 30 (NB).

HOUSE SPARROW   *Passer domesticus (B,W)*
Under-recorded (Ed).
F   40 Higgins Neuk 22 Aug (DF).
C   20 Alva 2 Nov (PMA). 30 Gartmorn 25 Dec (CJH).
S   14.4 pairs per sq km on Doune CBC only 63% of 1995; fledglings from
    7 Jun. 8th commonest species in Dunblane garden, max 14 (NB). 20
    Drip Carse 10 Oct, 20 Thornhill 25 Nov (CJH). 30 Killin 9 Aug (PWS).

TREE SPARROW   *Passer montanus (B,W)*
F   3 Bo'ness 3 Mar (AS). 5 Skinflats 11 Feb (IW). 3 pairs bred Dunmore
    (GB). 8 by R.Carron at Larbert 25 May & 6 on 6 Aug (MA).
C   4 Diverswell 15 May (CJH). 26 Gartmorn 6 Oct (WRB).
S   12 Stirling 21 Mar (IW). 20 Lecropt 4 Feb to 10 Mar, 30 on 23 Nov & 55
    on 21 Dec (MVB DT WRB). 3 Blairdrummond Carse 11 Feb & 6 on 10
    Apr (CJH IW). 50 Thornhill carse 30 Mar & 30 from late Sep to Dec
    (HK DR). 2 Arnprior 28 Apr & 12 Kippen 26 Oct (DAC).

CHAFFINCH   *Fringilla coelebs (B,W)*
F   40 Dunmore Oct to Dec (GB).
C   16 AoT on lower Devon in May, 13 in 1995 (CJH). 30 Alloa 22 Dec
    (BRT).
S   33.6 pairs per sq km on Doune CBC, much as 1995; fledging from 25
    Jun (NB). 450 Lecropt on 1 Jan & 500 on 28th (MVB). 250 in stubble
    Dunblane 8 Oct (CJH).

BRAMBLING   *Fringilla montifringilla (W)*
    Small numbers widespread
F   180 & 160 Slamannan 21 Jan. 6 Larbert 6 Apr & 2M on 9th (MA JMr).
C   15 Dollar 15 Jan, 7 Alva 11 Feb (AT PMA).
S   10 Arnprior 4 Feb & 12 on 10 Mar (DT DAC). 400 Cromlix on 1 Dec, 10
    Callander on 8th & 20 Kinbuck on 12th (MVB DJC).

GREENFINCH   *Carduelis chloris (B,W)*
    Underrecorded
S   1 AoT on Doune CBC, 3 in 1995. 3rd commonest species in Dunblane
    garden, max 20 on 14 Dec, few Jul-Oct (NB) - however: 42 nearby on
    26 Jun, odd date for flock (MVB).

GOLDFINCH   *Carduelis carduelis (B,W)*
F   25 Kinneil 29 Sep (AB). 14 Dunmore in Jul (GB).
C   3 AoT on lower Devon. 16 Cambus 21 Feb, 30 on 21 Aug & 40 on 13
    Oct (CJH WRB). 10 Alva 17 Dec (PMA). 40 Dollar 28 Dec (BRT).
S   3.6 pairs per sq km on Doune CBC, half 1995 (NB). Bred Buchlyvie &
    Dunblane (2 pairs) (DAC WRB). 17 Blairdrummond carse 11 Feb & 40
    Mid-Torrie 9 Mar (CJH BWB). 20 Gartmore on 15 Sep & 90 Arnprior
    on 22nd (DAC). 18 Dunblane 18 Oct; 70 BoA 24 Dec & 40 on 31st (CJH
    AT).

SISKIN   *Carduelis spinus (B,W)*
F   1 Skinflats 3 May (GO AB). 15 Polmont in Mar (JW).

C   30 Alva 31 Oct (PMA), 50 Dollar 8 Dec & 40 Gartmorn on 29th (RN AT). 45 east of Dollar 28 Dec, feeding in larches (BRT).
S   150 Kippen 2 Jan, 60 W of L.Watston on 16th (MT NB).14 L.Arklet 25 Apr (WRB). 50 Stronachlachar 25 Aug, 40+30 L.Ard 2 Nov (DAC); 100 L.Voil 26 Oct (WRB). 20 on roadside weeds Denny Muir 8 Nov & 50 Glen Vorlich on 9th (NB CJH). 24 in garden BoA 7 Dec, 70 on 8th & 18 on 27th (KD).

LINNET *Carduelis cannabina (B,W)*
F   530 Kinneil 3 Jan & 750 on 31st, 100 on 20 Mar, 200 on 7 Apr & 100 on 13 May; 75 on 14 Sep (MVB WRB AB DT). 80 east of Bonnybridge 14 Dec & 80 (2nd site) on 15th (MA).
C   40 Diverswell 19 Apr (CJH). 85 Gartmorn Jan-Feb (MC). 53 Kennetpans 10 Sep (CJH).
S   1 AoT on Doune CBC, 6 in 1995 - fallow field had been ploughed (NB). 4 AoT in gorse at Ashfield (WRB). 66 Blairdrummond carse 17 Jan; 550 Thornhill carse 15 Nov, 200 Kinbuck 8 Oct (CJH).

TWITE   *Carduelis flavirostris (b,W)*
F   43 Skinflats 27 Jan; 21 on 8 Dec (GO MVB). 150 Kinneil 1 Jan, last on 31 Mar (RS GO). 40 Higgins Neuk 9 Dec (DF).
C   2 in garden & on birdtable during snow near Dollar 27 Jan (RN). 4 below Lower Glendevon Res & 1 in song at Upper Res on 16 Jun (CJH).
S   2 Corriearklet in Apr (WRB). 3 Glen Lochay 14 Jul & 7 at two other sites on 4 Aug (RY). 2 Inverlochlarig 12 May & 4 Ben Ledi 14 Sep (DOE).

REDPOLL *Carduelis flammea (B,W)*
S   77 Sheriffmuir 26 Feb (AD). 4 at Stirling eating birch seed 8 Jan to 3 Mar (RJ). 1 Kippen Muir 17 Feb. 2 pairs Monachyle Glen 12 May (WRB). M (ringed) Buchlyvie 6 Aug - 1st in four years (DAC). 2 Hutchison Ptn 9 Nov (WRB).

COMMON CROSSBILL *Loxia curvirostra (b,W)*
S   At Carron Valley Forest: 8 on 17 Feb, then a few to Oct, small flocks in Dec (WRB AKM). 3 Invertrossachs 29 Mar. Max 3 Aberfoyle/L.Ard Forest 7 May to 2 Nov, 25 on 19 Nov (WRB CJH DAC DOE). 5 Cambusmore GP 8 Jun; 10 Flanders Moss, near Ward Toll, 31 Dec (CJH DT).

BULLFINCH *Pyrrhula pyrrhula (B,W)*
F   10 Howierigg Woods 7 Jan, 12 Darnrig Moss on 21st (MA). In spring/summer at Dunmore, Polmont & Haining Woods (Falkirk) (GB JW). 6 Blacknesss 11 Aug (AS).
S   Feeding on birdtable seed Stirling Feb (RJ). 3 cleared a Pyracantha bush of berries in Dec at Dunblane (NB). 7 L.Ard & 5 Menteith Hills 24 Jan (NB). 8 Ashfield 7 Mar (DAC). 7 in open heather at 400m Glen Casaig 15 Dec (CJH).

HAWFINCH   Coccothraustes coccothraustes   (?b,?w)
   No records received

*SNOW BUNTING   Plectrophenax nivalis (W)
S   5 Meall nan Each, Finglas, 20 Feb (CJH). 50 Cruach Ardrain 3 Mar
       (DOE).

YELLOWHAMMER   Emberiza citrinella (B,W)
C   14 AoT in 5 km on lower Devon, 8 in 1995 (CJH). 2 fed in garden at
       Alva 14 Mar, 1st in 24 years (PMA). 20 in garden Dollar 28 Jan (SH).
S   19.2 pairs per sq km on Doune CBC, as 1995, (NB). 90 Lecropt 1 Jan,
       80 on 8 Feb & 75 on 23 Mar, 25 on 23 Nov (MVB DAC WRB). 69
       Blairdrummond carse 9 Jan & 81 on 11 Feb (CJH). 30 Arnprior 11 Feb
       & 50 at 2nd site 16 Nov (DAC).

REED BUNTING   Emberiza schoeniclus (B,W)
C   2 AoT Cambus Pool 21 Apr, still nest with eggs 15 Aug (WRB). 13 Aot
       on Devon WBS, 10 in 1995 (CJH).
S   9 Blairdrummond carse 11 Feb (CJH). 2 pair on Doune CBC (NB). M
       Callander meadows 7 May & 2M Killin on 13th (PWS).

*CORN BUNTING   Emberiza calandra
       1 in song Skinflats 9 Jun (DMB). The last survivor in the area? Ed.

ESCAPED SPECIES

BLACK SWAN   Cygnus atratus
C   1 Cambus Pools 19 Jul (WRB).

MANDARIN   Aix galericulata
S   F Craigton Pond (Kinbuck) 10 Nov (WRB).

TURKEY VULTURE   Cathartes aura
S   On 30 Sep NB was told that a large bird of prey had been about North
       Third Res since May. He saw the bird that afternoon, using a x30
       telescope at a range of 200 m. It was larger than a Buzzard (at least
       twice the size of a nearby crow) and primarily black with silvery
       undersides to the primaries. The face was bare, red skin and the top
       of the head bare and black, the legs were reddish and it was ringed. It
       survived the winter, assisted by the provision of dead rabbits, eaten
       only when well rotted. NB saw it again on 4 Mar 1997, it was finally
       captured in April, then kept by the SSPCA until reclaimed by the
       owner from Duns. Apparently it had escaped in April 1996 and
       summered at St Abbs before wandering west.

RED-LEGGED/CHUKAR PARTRIDGE Alectoris chukar
S   5 Lecropt 13 Feb (AD). BoA, near golf course: 2 on 20 May, 1 on 17 &
       27 Jun (AT). 2, chicks about 2 weeks old, in garden at Dunblane 9 Jul;
       1 on garage roof 21 Sep (MVB).

Results of the BBS Surveys for Central Region

There were 9 squares, each 1x1 km, surveyed in our area in 1994, 10 in 1995 and 9.5 in 1996. Eight were the same in every year. In 1996 two were primarily suburban, 3 farmland (with some woodland), 2 upland heath and 1.5 conifer plantation. Almost 200 species were found in the UK BBS, in our area there were 78 species in 1994, 77 in 1995 and only 71 in 1996. Some of the more unusual species locally in 1994 were: Golden Plover, Sandwich Tern and Common Crossbill. Surprisingly there were no records of Moorhen, Whitethroat & Jay. In 1995 there were Osprey & Golden Plover but no Cormorant, Snipe, Common Sandpiper or Chiffchaff. In 1996 there was Cormorant, Moorhen, Snipe and Chiffchaff found on one square, with Whitethroat and Jay seen on 3 squares. Steve Sankey spotted an immature Golden Eagle on his remote hill square. None of the following were recorded:- Mute Swan, Red Grouse, Redshank, Common Sandpiper, Green Woodpecker, Great-spotted Woodpecker, Grey Wagtail (a poor year on CBC as well), Stonechat, Garden Warbler, Long-tailed Tit, Tree Creeper & Common Crossbill. *(Abstract of report by NB. Note the squares have been selected at random and each of two visits are made up of two transects of 1 km, both as straight as possible thus the occasional absence of some scarcer species is not surprising, Ed.)*

The average number of birds seen per visit per km^2 was 182 in 1994, 224 in 1995 & 197 in 1996.

Most Abundant Birds

1994		1995		1996	
1.	Chaffinch	1.	Starling	1.	Starling
2.	Meadow Pipit	2.	Chaffinch	2.	Chaffinch
3.	Blackbird	3.	Blackbird	3.	Meadow Pipit
4.	Woodpigeon	4.	Wren	4.	Blackbird
5.	Starling	5.	Woodpigeon	5.	Willow Warbler
6.	House Sparrow	6.	Rook	6.	Wood Pigeon
7.	Wren	7.	Coal Tit	7.	Carrion Crow
8.	Willow Warbler	8.	House sparrow	8.	House Sparrow
9=	Rook	9.	Meadow Pipit	9.	Rook
9=	Greenfinch	10.	Robin	10=	Wren
				10=	Blue Tit

WILDFOWL REPORT (1996-97)

This report covers the inland waters part of this area's Wetlands and Estuary Bird Survey (WEBS) organised by NB and is a condensed version of a fuller report by him.

WeBS is a monthly waterfowl census under the auspices of the British Trust for Ornithology (BTO) and the Wildfowl & Wetlands Trust (WWT). Although WeBS counts can be made all year round this report deals only with the 'core' months (the 'season') which runs from September to March inclusive. For this report 'wildfowl' includes divers, grebes, cormorants, herons, swans, geese (excluding Pink-footed and Greylag for which the WWT organises separate counts), ducks and rails.

When interpreting the various statistics in this report please bear in mind that Coot and Great Crested Grebe were not counted until 1982-3, Little Grebe until 1985-6 and Cormorants until 1986-7. Mallard come in three categories: Mallard 1 are totally wild receiving no human assistance; Mallard 2 are wild but are fed in some way by humans; Mallard 3 owe their existence to humans being reared by them, released onto shooting ponds and fed for their short lifes.

This report covers the area occupied by the new local government councils of Stirling, Falkirk and Clackmannanshire (the 'region'). In total, 109 still water sites, 113.2km of river and 24.4km of canal were counted by 47 counters.

Still Water Sites

Standing water in Central Region amounts to 7693 hectares or 2.9 % of the area.

The total figures, excluding Mallard, suggest that wildfowl numbers for 1996/7 were only 2 % down on the previous season but 31 % up on 1994/5. Matched monthly data taken from 14 sites in the top 25 are shown in Table 1. Those sites holding fed Mallard have been excluded.

Table 1	1994/5	1995/6	1996/7	No of Sites
September	246	539	612	9
October	2284	3294	1955	13
November	2476	3582	3209	14
December	2741	4458	3874	14
January	3048	2838	4351	14
February	2642	2683	2717	14
March	1469	1745	1617	14
Totals	14906	19139	18335	

This table corroborates the remarks above, with last seasons numbers down 4 % on the previous season and up 23 % on 1994/5. WeBS counts in the recording area started in 1960 but coverage varied greatly from year to year and was never as complete as for the past three seasons. In an attempt to see if the counts for the past two seasons do represent an increase in wildfowl numbers I have been able to compare monthly averages for 9 of the sites using the data from 1960-1994 in comparison to the mean for 1995/6 and 1996/7 combined. This shows that the past two seasons are 4.7 % up on 1960-94 and the 1994/5 season was 30 % down on the 1960-94 average.

Concentrating on the 96/7 season, the October total was the lowest in the past 3 years, probably because the unusually mild weather that month delayed the birds departure from Northern and mainland Europe. Numbers built up through November and December to peak in January, a month later than the previous season. The February and March totals have been fairly consistent over the last 3 seasons with a general upward trend, although March 97's total was a little down on that of '96, probably due to the mild weather which possibly encouraged the birds to return early to their breeding grounds.

Turning to individual sites, the top ten along with monthly averages are listed below:- (previous seasons figures in brackets)

	Site	Average
1. (1)	Gartmorn Dam	1300 (1302)
2. (3)	Lake of Menteith	264 (264)
3. (4)	Gart Complex	243 (245)
4. (-)	Loch Earn	217 (226)
5. (2)	Airthrey Loch	181 (279)
6. (6)	Blairdrummond Park	178 (173)
7. (9)	Carron Valley Resr.	164 (146)
8. (21)	L. Lomond at Balmaha	149 (74)
9. (27)	Kersiepow Ponds	136 (57)
10. (5)	Vale of Coustry	128 (211)

The above table excludes sites where mallard are reared and released for shooting.

As shown above, Gartmorn is still far and away the most populous site, holding 4.9 times more than the Lake of Menteith, it also accounts for 23.8 % of all still water birds in the region. This season's monthly average is just below the medium term average of 1332 (MTA dates back to 1982-3 when Coot and Great Crested Grebe were first included in the counts).Gartmorn also had the highest average with the ubiquitous Mallard excluded and the most species with 18.

The Gart Complex close to Callander has also returned a monthly average close to the previous season's. Part of this complex is still an active sand and gravel pit and over the next 20 years it is proposed to extract gravel over much of the area now being counted. An environmental survey and report have been undertaken, this will be used to create a rolling plan which should minimise the disturbance to the birds. In the long term the result will be a wildlife haven with a water body roughly five times the area of what is currently extant.

Linear Water Features: Rivers & Canals

This season saw a large increase in the length of these features counted. Rivers rose from 47 km to 113.2 km and canals from 9.6 km to 24.4 km. This means that almost all of the sections of river thought to be worth counting were covered and all of the canals in the region were counted. The number of counters on these linear water features rose from 8 to 34.

Still waters accounted for 76 % of the region's wildfowl (Gartmorn Dam alone accounts for 18 %) and linear waters for 24 %. The total length of 113.2 km. of river was never counted in any one month but in January and March over 100 km. was counted, this coincided with full coverage of the canals and resulted in 23 % and 27 % of the region's totals for the respective months. As stated earlier, there is roughly 7693 Ha. of standing water in the region which gives a monthly average of 0.6 birds Ha^{-1}. Using an average width of 20 m for the linear features gives an area of 320 Ha, thus higher density of 4.6 birds Ha^{-1}.

Table 2 Percentages of the more common species on still and linear sites.

	Still	Linear
Little Grebe	74	26
Great Crested Grebe	100	0
Cormorant	68	32
Grey Heron	51	49
Mute Swan	56	44
Whooper Swan	60	40
Canada Goose	100	0
Wigeon	75	25
Teal	64	36
Wild Mallard	65	35
Pochard	98	2
Tufted Duck	95	5
Goldeneye	73	27
Red-breasted Merganser	2	98
Goosander	66	34
Moorhen	32	68
Coot	99.6	0.4

Table 2 shows that linear waters are favoured by Moorhen and Red-breasted Merganser whereas Great Crested Grebe and Canada Goose are totally absent, Coot and Pochard are unusual and Tufted Duck scarce. For the remaining 10 species 25-50 % of the region's numbers are to be found on linear waters.

WEBS contributors to these data additional to report list were: M. Callan, Z. Clayson, M. Cooper, P. Dearing, A. Hibbert, M. Kobs, G.&E. Leisk, D. Mason, D. Minard, J. Nimmo, L. O'Toole, J. Peterson, D. Series, N. Sharpe, D. Shenton, H. Weir.

REVIEWS (Naturalist)

Where to Watch Birds in Scotland. M. Malders and J. Welstead. 3rd edition. 1997. C. Helm. 330pp. ISBN 0-7136-4487-7. £12.99.

Previous editions 1989 and 1993. It includes Central area pp32-46 with notes on The Forth, Inches, Cambus, Lake of Menteith, Pass of Leny, Inversnaid, Inchcailloch, Gartmorn, Doune Park.... It has in it a code of conduct, a systematic list, and notes on loch reports and records which include FNH.

L.C.

A Guide to British Birds (Wings). Two video 95 minute tapes of the full Channel 4 television series made in conjunction with RSPB. Wings 3, Channel Four Video, PO Box 6120, London, W12 8VG. £10.99 each.

A comprehensive guide both to birds, their splendours and enigmas, and to the people who watch them.

THE CURRENT STATUS OF THE RAVEN AS A BREEDING SPECIES IN CENTRAL SCOTLAND

P. Stirling-Aird

This paper gives details of the current status of the Raven *Corvus corax* in the part of Central Scotland described in the paper *The decline of the Raven as a breeding species in Central Scotland* (Mitchell, 1981) and draws comparisons with the survey results mentioned in that paper. The study area comprises the Highland parts of former Stirlingshire and south-west Perthshire south of Glen Lochy, Strath Fillan and the Glen Dochart/Glen Lochay watershed plus the outlying Lowland ranges of the Campsie, Fintry and Gargunnock Hills. The paper remarks on the status of Ravens elsewhere in Scotland, primarily in the adjoining area of Tayside.

The Ravens of this study area are almost exclusively crag nesters although in recent years and just outside the study area, nests have been discovered in a very few Scots Pines. While most pairs nest at medium altitudes in the hill ground, i.e. around the 1,500 (460 m) to 2,000 feet (615 m) level, there are a few nesting records from (in the British context) both very low and very high altitudes. One Raven pair nests intermittently at the 500 feet (155 m) level in an isolated crag in the middle of a conifer plantation while another pair in remote hill sheep and deer forest county has been found to have one of its alternative nesting sites at the 2,750 feet (845 m) level.

Mitchell's 1981 paper cites late 18th century changes in the area concerned, from a cattle and goat economy to one of sheep farming, this increasing the food supply of Ravens but (together with game preservation which was then in the ascendency) inviting their persecution. These changes were followed by probable stabilisation of the Raven population after 1939 but a slow but steady disappearance of Ravens in approximately the 15 years prior to 1981. By then 12 of the 30 known breeding territories in the area had been deserted, the greatest decline being in the southern half of the survey area where by the early 1970s at six territories (of which one was occupied only irregularly) only a single pair was recorded.

Possible causes for the decline considered by Mitchell were: increased competition for nest sites from an expanding Peregrine *Falco peregrinus* population; large scale afforestation resulting in removal of sheep stocks and loss of open habitat; improvements in sheep stock management leading to lowered sheep mortality and a reduction in carrion on the hill; susceptibility of Ravens to organo-chlorine insecticides used in sheep dips; increased use of poisoned baits for controlling foxes, crows, etc; and increased recreational disturbance of nesting Ravens. The conclusion was that, while conversion of sheep walk to plantation forestry had contributed to the abandonment of several Raven territories, there had been virtually no afforestation in the southern part of the area where most losses of breeding Ravens had occurred. Having dismissed increased Peregrine numbers, pesticide use and recreational activity as significant contributory factors, Mitchell suggested that changes in sheep husbandry and use of poison baits warranted further investigation as apparent causes of this decline.

In 1981, in the 18 Raven territories (30 in all were checked) where occupation was recorded (by 17 pairs with one single bird seen) 11 pairs were found to be nesting; the figures in Mitchell's 1981 paper are adjusted to allow for one breeding pair whose existence was not known at the time that that paper was published. A 1987 survey of 27 of the 30 previously known territories revealed a broadly similar picture of occupation, with 10 territories being apparently unoccupied and 14 pairs found to be nesting in the remaining 17 occupied territories. However, by 1996, in the course of a survey of nearly all known Raven breeding territories the then local government areas of Central and Tayside Regions, only 6 out of 28 of the territories examined in 1981 were found to be unoccupied. In 1996 nesting took place certainly in 17 of the 22 occupied territories with 11 pairs producing young. Table 1 compares the years 1981 and 1996 for the numbered territories listed in Mitchell's paper and includes details of seven additional territories checked in 1996 that were either unknown or not visited in 1981.

A possible reason for the recent increase in breeding Ravens, given Mitchell's earlier suggestions, is a decrease in poisoning as a result of public campaigning against this illegal practice. Recent adoption of the live catching Larsen trap for corvids, a legal game management tool, may have helped the situation as some gamekeepers who have seen its effectiveness have apparently stopped putting out poison baits. In addition, and notwithstanding possible changes in sheep management leading to a reduced carrion food supply for Ravens from this source, by contrast in recent years an expanding rabbit population may have resulted in more food for Ravens. The diet of the non-breeding wintering population of Ravens in Tayside was found to be mainly rabbits and hares. Nevertheless food supply appears to be a limiting factor in the case of certain Raven pairs in the southern part of the study area, where in 1996, although several territories were occupied, only one pair produced young; removal of sheep stock from some of the ground is implicated. By contrast, recreational disturbance (including that caused by hang-gliding and para-gliding) has almost certainly increased since 1981.

There is an intriguing although so far as is known hitherto unsubstantiated suggestion that radioactive fallout from the 1986 Chernobyl nuclear accident in the former Soviet Union could have affected Raven productivity in certain parts of Britain, and presumably by implication other species also. In *The Independent* of 22nd August 1988 there was a report (by Geoffrey Horne) that in the Lake District feeding on carrion might have affected the Raven's reproductive system. Tests by the Ministry of Agriculture had shown that many sheep flocks in the Lake District had above normal post-Chernobyl radiation levels and in that area 24 out 36 Raven pairs failed to rear young in 1988.

Looking to a slightly wider picture, preliminary results of the 1996 Central and Tayside Raven survey show 88 territories checked with 64 pairs (of which 35 nested successfully) and one single bird recorded, while 23 territories were found to be apparently unoccupied. In Central Scotland illegal persecution of Ravens may be at a minimal level. In Tayside, where there is more interest in game (especially Red Grouse) management, apparent natural non-occupation of Raven territories and breeding failure could be masking persecution; two such instances are known to have occurred in Tayside in 1996. Breeding Ravens are conspicuously absent from large areas of apparently suitable habitat in the north and east of Tayside. Parallel increases of breeding Ravens have occurred in southern Scotland (where to some extent deer and goat carrion may have replaced sheep carrion lost as a result of afforestation and where more rabbit carrion has become available on sheep walks). There have also been slight signs of increases in north-east Scotland in recent years. Raven increases in all areas may nevertheless do no more than compensate for or perhaps may not even equal decreases that have taken place since the 1960s. As with so many other species, the Raven's future depends closely on land management practices.

Table 1 Territory occupation by Ravens in Central Scotland in 1981 and 1996

(The category "Pair with nest" for 1981 may be taken to mean in many, probably most, cases that the nest contained young.)

Territory number	Field observation in 1981	Field observation in 1996
1	Apparently unoccupied	Pair with young
2	Apparently unoccupied	Pair present
3	Pair with nest	Apparently unoccupied
4	Apparently unoccupied	Pair present
5	Apparently unoccupied	Apparently unoccupied
6	Apparently unoccupied	Apparently unoccupied
7	Pair present	No information
8	Pair behaving as if with nest	Pair with nest (failed)
9	Pair with nest	Pair apparently present
10	Pair present	Apparently unoccupied
11	Apparently unoccupied	Pair with young
12	Pair with nest	Pair with nest (failed)
13	Single bird only	Pair with young
14	Pair with young	Pair with nest (failed)
15	Apparently unoccupied	Pair with young
16	Apparently unoccupied	Pair with young
17	Probably occupied	Pair with young
18	Pair with nest	Pair with young
19	Pair with nest	Apparently unoccupied
20	Pair present	Pair with nest (failed)

21	Apparently unoccupied	Pair with young
22	Apparently unoccupied	Apparently unoccupied
23	Apparently unoccupied	Pair present
24	Pair present	Pair with nest (failed)
25	Pair present	Pair present
26	Pair with nest	Pair with nest (failed)
27	Pair with nest	Pair with young
28	Pair with nest	Pair with young
29	Apparently unoccupied	No information
30	Pair with nest	Pair with young
31	—	Pair with nest (failed)
32	—	Pairs present
33	—	Pair with young
34	—	Apparently unoccupied
35	—	Apparently unoccupied
36	—	Apparently unoccupied
37	—	Pair with young

Acknowledgements

My thanks are due to a number of observers who have produced Raven breeding records over the years. I am indebted to John Mitchell and Wendy Mattingley for providing information on Raven territory occupation and breeding performance in Central and Tayside Regions respectively and for commenting on the draft of this paper. Derek Ratcliffe's definitive work on the bird (Ratcliffe, 1997), has been a valuable source of reference.

References

Mitchell, J. (1981). The decline of the Raven as a breeding species in Central Scotland. *Forth Naturalist and Historian* 6, 35-42.

Ratcliffe, D. (1997). *The Raven*. London: T. and A. D. Poyser.

REVIEWS (Naturalist)

Butterfly Conservation Newsletter, 4. East of Scotland Branch. April 1997.

Includes: Success of campaign to prevent a major opencast mining application at Greenbank, Kelty: Records of sightings 19996 by recorder Chris Stamp – 10 1 cm square location maps for eight species: Bar charts of 101 cm square records for 11 common and 13 uncommon species: Evaluation of eye spots colouring.

Butterfly Conservation. A large membership pack sponsored by BP is available to applicants to join the Society for Butterfly Conservation which has Scottish Branches.

L.C.

THE CHEQUERED SKIPPER AND BUTTERFLY CONSERVATION IN SCOTLAND

David Spooner

A key date in the development of butterfly conservation in Scotland was the publication of *Butterflies in Scotland* (Thomson, 1980). This brilliant conspectus of the history of each of the nation's 37 butterflies covered the past 150 years of sightings. It was the moment when modern methods were brought to bear on lepidopteral studies, and in its comprehensiveness and readability it has not been equalled in England. Prior to Thomson's work, much of the data had come from the antiquaries-cum-naturalists to whom so much is owed for the pre-1939 records.

The British Butterfly Conservation Society, on the other hand, is relatively new on the scene in Scotland, the Western Branch based in Kelvingrove Museum & Gallery dating from 1985. The society as a whole was established in 1968 by an amateur entomologist, Thomas Frankland, with Peter Scott as its founding president. Frankland's Dedham house from which the organisation grew remains the administrative centre. The primary function of Butterfly Conservation with its three Scottish branches is to monitor the habitats of threatened butterflies and moths, and to ensure their survival. The crux of lepidopterology is in identifying the exact requirements of the insect, including the minutiae of the larval and imaginal food plants in regard to temperature and maturity, and managing the habitat to ensure the necessary conditions. Often this demands such activities as coppicing for the preservation of sunny south-facing rides for the nectar needs of the butterfly. This itself is far from the days when coppicing was a natural part of small-scale wood management where Thomas Hardy could casually write:

I leant upon a coppice gate/When Frost was spectre-gray.

The work done on the Chequered Skipper, *Carterocephalus palaemon*, is a good example (Figure 1). Until its recent reintroduction into England from French sources it had been specific to Northwest Scotland after its disappearance south of the border in 1976 (Figure 2). As an indication of the state of records until recently, the first definitive sighting dates from a specimen of June 1939. The Scottish Wildlife Trust undertook a number of surveys in the 1970s, discovering many new localities, at which point the Nature Conservancy Council extended the monitoring, and finally Butterfly Conservation came up with a comprehensive Species Action Plan. It is now known in some 50 locations, but is usually seen in low numbers. The centre of the population is Fort William near the site of its original discovery around oak woodlands on the flood plant of the River Lochy (Figures 3 and 4).

When I see this beautiful butterfly I am put in mind of it as a symbol of the '45 since it flies at Glenfinnan. I put this into a poem, part of which runs:

"rowan ripeness
for fantailed fantastic siskin
darting, or palaemon
flicker across grass.
These remain.

Heroics, loyalty, dashed
to a broken oar
never planted in foreign shore

unchosen distance
shattered space."

The Chequered Skipper is an energetic creature, and needs large amounts of sun and nectar to flourish. Eggs are laid on tussocks of purple moor-grass (*Molina caerula*), and its flies from May to June. The reason the French *palaemon* was used as the basis for its reintroduction into England is that the continental butterfly utilises the same food plants as the English Skipper: Purple Small-reed, Wood Small-reed and Wood False-brome. As Ravenscroft (1996) puts it in his excellent booklet on this butterfly:

> All these grasses share one feature. They have wide blades, which the larvae of the Chequered Skipper, in common with its grass feeding relatives, the Small, Essex and Large Skippers, require to make protective shelters.

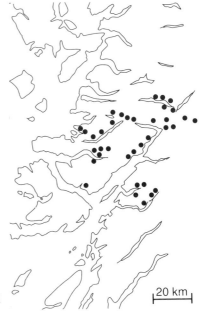

Figure 1 The Chequered Skipper.

Figure 2 Distribution of the Chequered Skipper in Northwest Scotland.

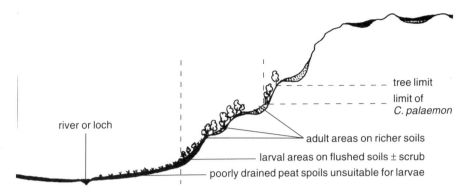

river or loch

tree limit

limit of
C. palaemon

adult areas on richer soils

larval areas on flushed soils ± scrub

poorly drained peat spoils unsuitable for larvae

Figure 3 Typical Chequered Skipper site in Scotland. Black areas show peat; stippled areas brown forest soils.

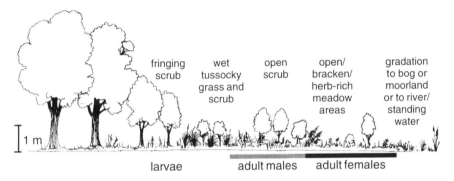

1 m

fringing scrub

wet tussocky grass and scrub

open scrub

open/ bracken/ herb-rich meadow areas

gradation to bog or moorland or to river/ standing water

larvae   adult males   adult females

Figure 4 The Skipper's woodland edge habitat.

Likewise the Scottish *palaemon* larva wraps itself in purple moor-grass during the summer to hibernate during the winter.

But sheep-grazing and rapid tree growth can very easily lead to local extinction. It has disappeared from Glen Nevis because of over-grazing. As so often in the complex age of biodiversity, there are serious conflicts of species and land-use interests. Woodland grant schemes, which involve fencing areas to exclude animals and allow regeneration of natural woodland, threaten the habitats. At the moment we are striving to increase the number of protected sites which presently number a mere three, two managed by SNH and one by the SWT. Joint action is being carried out with Scottish Hydro-Electric whose coppicing of wayleaves for their power lines creates clearings where nectar and plants and grasses can develop.

Like the Kentish Glory Moth, the New Forest Burnet (*Zygaena viciae argyllensis*) now only flies in Scotland. In the case of this Burnet – whose English subspecies *Z. v. tenensis* died out in the 1920 – it survives on a small ledge which had been missed by grazing sheep. It was discovered originally only in the 1960s, then rediscovered by David Balfour in 1989 though only a handful had survived. This has now been fenced by SNH. Scotland is home to six of the seven Burnets in the British Isles and all except the common Six-Spot are in immediate danger from the ever-expanding bracken. More research is required in the Northwest and Inner Hebrides.

Butterflies, and moths arguably to a lesser extent, rare moths react badly to changes in their grass land rides. They are insects of habit. But the fact is that large areas of Central Scotland are becoming inhospitable to lepidoptera due to the progressive disappearance of the relatively specialised habitats that they require. In 1994 I wrote in a burst of fitful optimism in *Butterfly Conservation News*:

> I did come across an exceptionally early Large Heath in its *polydama* form down from the uplands in mid-May 1992 … The deindustrialisation of central Scotland may hopefully have the side effect of encouraging species to venture further south.

However the closure of so many deep-mined pits over the past decade, partly at least as the result of government policy, has led to the proliferation of opencast mining. Butterfly Conservation Society has successfully assisted in the campaign to halt two such mines in Fife and Clackmannan, saving the plants and creatures from the depredations of this sterilisation of the ground. Nevertheless whole swathes of countryside in Lanarkshire, Ayrshire and indeed Fife and Clackmannan that have survived road- and house-building programmes are falling prey to opencast developments. It is often a strategically placed farm that is the target. One area of Lanarkshire near Airdrie is already so battle-scarred, it has been chosen as the setting for the film of Pat Barker's Booker-prize trilogy of First World War novels.

Ultimately the only answer is a greatly extended policy of purchase of key habitats, along with a policy and legal curb on the decimations of opencasting. Otherwise the shadow of wartorn landscape will come to dominate the lowland Central Belt, and remove the last of the rarer animals that depend upon specialised habitats.

References

Thomson, G. (1980). *The Butterflies of Scotland.* Croom Helm, London.
Ravenscroft, N. (1996). *The Chequered Skipper.* Butterfly Conservation Society, Dedham, Essex.

Footnotes

To George Thomson's 36 resident and migrant butterflies of Scotland needs to be added the Gatekeeper, recorded by the Institute for Terrestrial Ecology on a number of occasions since 1995.

For the future, the Comma had reached north Northumberland by 1995, and may well not have been noticed in the Scottish Borders because of the scarcity of Recorders there.

FIRST IN FISH CULTURE
SIR JAMES MAITLAND (1848-1897) AND HOWIETOUN
People of the Forth (11)

Stephen Hill

From as long ago as the days of Ancient China – since at least 2698BC to be more precise – man has in some way farmed fish. In the 'early days' this involved little more than simply holding and rearing fish in ponds in order to fatten them for the table but, after a discovery in the mid-eighteenth century by a Westphalian landowner named Stephan Jacobi, it became possible for man actually to propagate fish through the manipulation of external fertilisation. By this method, ova were released from the female (achieved by a gentle stroke of the fish's stomach) and mixed with milt (sperm) extricated from a male in a similar manner. The fertilised eggs were therefore able to be kept in a protected environment, shielded from problems inherent with incubation in the wild such as flooding and predators, and young fish hatched out and reared in much the same way as livestock are farmed.[1] In the 250 years since this discovery fish farming (pisciculture) has grown dramatically. In 1990, in Britain alone, there were 769 registered fish farming businesses whilst in 1987, globally, 14.5 million tonnes of farmed fish and shellfish were produced, amounting to 12.3 % of the total world fish and shellfish harvest.[2]

The far greater part of this explosion in pisciculture has taken place in the twentieth century with its beginnings traceable to the latter half of the nineteenth century when a general concern arose in the industrial nations of Western Europe and North America that nature's supplies of fish, mainly of salmon and trout, but also of some sea fish varieties, were dwindling as a result of over-fishing, a lack of statutory protection and industrial pollution. This concern led to a considerable number of people in various countries taking up fish farming and thereby trying to redress the damage done to nature's own supplies of fish. One of these was a Stirlingshire man, Sir James Ramsay Gibson Maitland (1848-1897), incumbent of the Bannockburn and Sauchie Estates and also of Edinburgh's Barnton Estate. Before commencing pisciculture in 1873 Maitland had attended the University of St Andrews and then gone on to Sandhurst before entering the army with a commission as Cornet in the Fourth Dragoon Guards. He also took an active role in local politics as a member of the local council. This article is concerned only with Maitland's piscicultural work and contends that Maitland was not just one of many early pisciculturalists but a pioneer and as yet unsung hero who blazed the trails and played a pivotal role in the development of today's massive global fish farming industry.

Maitland began piscicultural experiments in autumn 1873 with the impregnation of 2-3,000 trout ova taken from spawners in Loch Leven. A further 20-30,000 ova were taken in 1874 and in 1875 he constructed a hatchery at Howietoun on the Sauchie Estate about five miles from Stirling, with a capacity for 260,000 ova. By 1878 he had transformed his original take of a few thousand ova from Loch Leven to a stock of 13,593 young fish. From 1879, the Howietoun Fishery, as it became known, began selling fertilised eggs and live fish to landowners, angling associations and public bodies such as local councils, all of whom were desirous of restocking their depleted freshwaters. In 1883 the fishery was extended with the construction of a new hatchery covering 3,000 square feet and capable of incubating millions of eggs, a despatching house, a fish food preparation house and offices for the growing number of staff. By 1885 demand for the fishery's produce was growing so fast that Maitland was easily able to sell some 100,000 live fish, and had to increase his incubation capacity to 20 million eggs. The fishery was finally completed in 1886, comprising two huge hatcheries and 33 ponds covering nine acres and housing a stock of 282,672 live fish.

So what did pisciculture at Howietoun entail that justifies the assertion made above that Maitland's work deserves historical recognition? *Prima facie*, the distinction between Howietoun and other contemporary fisheries was that it was a fully fledged *commercial* fish *farm* which sold eggs and fish on the open market. This made it quite distinct from others, such as those at Galway in Ireland and Stormontfield at Perth which had been set up by fishery owners and intended to restock only one particular waterway. Indeed, Howietoun's trade was such that, by 1886, "on most of the principal lines of railway, the Howietoun tanks are nearly as well known as the milk cans."[3]

The next factor marking Howietoun was its size. In 1880, it became the largest piscicultural operation in the United Kingdom.[4] The Stormontfield operation on the Tay, for example, had used only a handful of small ponds, whereas Howietoun had 33 large ones. Stormontfield had been run single-handedly by its operator, Robert Buist; Howietoun, on the other hand, required the services of Maitland, a manager, seven operatives, four labourers, two carpenters and a part-time secretary.[5] By 1885, Howietoun had an annual incubation capacity of 20 million ova whilst Stormontfield could handle only a maximum 300,000 ova per annum.[6] Even Howietoun's next largest contemporary establishment, Thomas Andrews' Guildford Fishery, could only handle four million ova per annum after being considerably enlarged in 1887.[7] By early 1886, Howietoun was one of 11 hatcheries in Scotland but its annual produce was three times as great as that of the others put together.[8]

Howietoun was the largest single salmonoid piscicultural establishment in the world.[9] In 1883, the combined total output of salmonoid fry from all 11 hatcheries in Canada, for example, amounted to 5,649,000 whilst Howietoun alone produced 6,600,000.[10] In 1886, the largest hatchery operated by the United States Commission on Fish and Fisheries covered 1,500 square feet which was less than half the size of Howietoun's principal hatchery.[11] As late as 1893, the largest hatcheries on continental Europe, at Selzenhof and Seewiese in Germany, could only produce eight and four million salmonoid eggs per annum respectively, against Howietoun's 20 million.[12] As a correspondent of

The Times, Henry Ffennell, noted of Maitland's creation in 1886:
Here we have a fish farm which certainly has no equal in the United Kingdom, while, from what I hear on good authority, I believe there is nothing to compare to it in the United States, in Canada, or on the continent.[13]

Where Howietoun really differed, however, was in the *quality* of its product, in terms of both hatching survival rates and of the vitality of the fish produced. From 1876, Maitland's hatchery was delivering alevins (tadpole-like baby fish) from eggs with only a 10 % loss in hatching, far less than that experienced by other pisciculturalists of the day.[14] The loss at Huningue, a large hatchery in France, for example, had amounted to between 60 and 70 %.[15] At Stormontfield, it had been as much as 80 to 90 %.[16] After 1876, as the size of Howietoun and Maitland's skill grew, hatching success rates increased to 93.3 %, rising further to 95-99 % by the mid-1880s.[17] A higher loss "would be considered extraordinary at Howietoun".[18]

The reason for such impressive success rates – and Maitland's most important contribution to piscicultural science – was his use of stock fish for breeding. As he himself put it: "It is here that Howietoun has worked a revolution in fish culture."[19] All earlier pisciculturalists had procured ova and milt from parent fish on the point of spawning naturally in their wild environment. Maitland's work was different. Initially taking a supply of ova and milt from wild breeders in Loch Leven between 1873 and 1877, Maitland kept a supply of his artificially propagated progeny at Howietoun and thereby bred a stock of domesticated trout with which to fulfil his future requirements for parent fish. Howietoun became self-sufficient in its needs for ova and milt, entirely devoid of reliance on the natural environment, and had a captive broodstock of 11,000 trout of which 7,000 per annum were always in prime condition and ready to spawn. This shielded Howietoun from the uncertainties of relying on the capture of wild spawners which had plagued earlier pisciculturalists. Maitland could acquire between 0.3 and 0.5 million eggs in a single morning whilst it took the operators of the Dupplin hatchery on the Tay, for example, – the successor to Stormontfield – 22 days to secure 360,000 eggs from wild parents.[20]

More importantly, the use of a domesticated broodstock led to Maitland's discovery that the quality of artificially propagated fish could actually be enhanced, by the careful selection of parent fish, such that they became superior to those naturally propagated in the wild. After carefully studying fish bred from parents of varying ages, Maitland realised that a clear positive correlation existed between the age and size of the parent fish and the vitality of their progeny.[21] Eggs procured from big, older spawners were larger in size (with a relatively lower number of ova per female fish), more resistant to damage and less likely to abort during gestation than those taken from smaller, younger spawners. Four-year-old fish, for example, produced eggs that numbered 32 per length of glass grille in the fishery's hatching trays whilst the eggs of six-year-old fish numbered only 27 per grille. Ova from two- and three-year-old fish averaged 0.17 inches in diameter whilst that from six year olds averaged 0.18 to 0.19 inches, and that from eight year olds between 0.2 and 0.22 inches.[22] The fry produced from such larger eggs were found to grow into larger and stronger adult fish with a greater life expectancy than the progeny of younger, unselected parents.[23]

By deciding to use only mature parent fish, Maitland improved the quality of the breed of trout initially taken from Loch Leven in the mid-1870s. Whilst the ova of wild fish in Loch Leven ran at 40,000 to the gallon, the ova of Howietoun-bred Loch Levens by 1886 ran at 23-26,000 to the gallon. This was the same size as the ova of the trout's more fashionable cousin, the *Salmo Salar*, which, on the River Tay, ran at 25,000 to the gallon. Putting it another way, 1,250 Loch Leven ova spawned from the Howietoun fish in 1886 occupied the same space as 2,500 ova from wild spawners in Loch Leven and 1,350 Tay salmon ova. Whilst the average weight of the spawning fish performing natural reproduction in Loch Leven was 1.5 pounds, the Howietoun spawners weighed in at between seven and eight pounds.[24] The *Field* greeted Maitland's discovery most enthusiastically, remarking that it gave Howietoun's fish an "extraordinary vigour and vitality, ... [they] ... could stand almost any vicissitude".[25]

So, Howietoun was unique in both quality and quantity. But the acid test of Maitland's importance in piscicultural development has to be whether his work was a crucial phase in the development of the science of the modern aquaculture industry, with his discoveries continuing to play an important role in pisciculture well after his death in 1897. That this is in fact the case is beyond doubt. The new techniques which were developed at Howietoun in the 1880s remain the cornerstone of modern pisciculture. Maitland disseminated his knowledge through a large number of publications including his 1886 *History of Howietoun* which set out the fishery's methods in great detail – principally the selective breeding of fish from a captive broodstock within the overall framework of a large scale professional operation. It is, of course, impossible definitively to state that Maitland 'invented' modern pisciculture, but it is clear that modern pisciculture reflects his findings and that there is no evidence of such work, either in terms of its discoveries or its size, having taken place before him.

Maitland's significance can be assessed in a global context by looking at late nineteenth century fish culture in the United States, the most pisciculturally active nation of the late nineteenth and early twentieth centuries when it enjoyed a huge centrally financed and directed fish cultural effort under the auspices of the United States Commission on Fish and Fisheries. Massive though this operation was, with a rash of hatcheries across the length and breadth of America, Howietoun was still bigger than any individual United States hatchery.[26]

The contention that Howietoun's pisciculture was in advance of that in North America is supported by early twentieth century North American piscicultural literature. In an article by Arthur Sykes on selective breeding in the 1902 volume of the *Transactions of the American Fisheries Society*, it was noted that: "Much has been said and written about methods and results of propagation; but little thought, it seems, has been given to the foundation on which we work or the quality of the material of which it is comprised, *ie.*, the potency and vigour of the parent fish and the embryo." He argued that American pisciculture should look to an enhancement of the quality of its product through selective breeding rather than by using spawning fish of any size or age taken from the wild. He then gave a clear recognition of the importance of Maitland's work, albeit in a way that failed to recognise that Maitland had carried out such work more than 20 years previously:

> Sir James Gibson-Maitland, Scotland's greatest fish culturalist, … said 'Civilisation must breed its trout as its cattle, or civilisation will have no trout.' *The truth of this statement is evident to me, though I have no doubt he wrought better than he knew.*[27]

Indeed, American experiments in selective broodstock breeding only came about some four decades after Maitland's own work, with the experiments of Hayford and Embody from 1919. They found that a "marked increase in the rate of growth … resulted from a selection of the largest breeders".[28] As late as 1938, an employee of the United States Commission on Fish and Fisheries clearly indicated how advanced Maitland's work had been and how slow had been his American contemporaries and, indeed, their immediate heirs:

> It is all too apparent that progress has been much slower than it might have been…. The early fish culturist had his problems but no one will deny that, in general, they were much simpler than those which confront his present day successor. All that was necessary was to strip the eggs from wild fish, incubate them in hatchery troughs and, as soon as the fry were able to feed, turn them loose to fend for themselves…. SELECTIVE BREEDING So far, few attempts have been made to improve trout by this technique…. If but a very small proportion of the amount now expended on hatchery operations could be devoted to research and experiment and to the training of men in better fish cultural practises, the history of the next 25 years would be quite different from that of the past – and it would no longer be necessary to apologise for the shortcomings of our hatcheries.[29]

When Maitland died, in 1897 of a gouty infection at the age of only 49, his obituarists paid due acknowledgement to his "success in pisciculture" at Howietoun, "one of the most successful fish hatchery establishments in the world".[30] His local minister, the Rev J.M. Robertson of St Ninian's Parish Church, was sure that Maitland's "reputation as a public benefactor" would long be preserved because of his "labours and efforts in the domain of natural history".[31] But the renown of his work, both generally and specifically, seems to have died with him, thereby denying him an historical niche. Maitland is referred to in only four modern works, and even then only in passing and without any real substance. Of these four works, one mentions merely that he was involved in early exports of salmon and trout ova to the Antipodes,[32] and another notes that he was a "pioneer of freshwater fish farming who had established a successful hatchery".[33] Of the two other works, one refers to him incorrectly as Sir Thomas Maitland of Howietown (sic) and says nothing more[34] and the other states that he was a "notable trout farmer" but with no detail on what he actually achieved.[35]

Maitland's neglect by historians becomes even more apparent when one looks at the survival of his name in relation to his specific legacy to pisciculture, the development of selective breeding from a captive broodstock in order to enhance the quality of the product. A twentieth century commentator on pisciculture, for example, noted that: "Fish culture to be classed as a science must include ... a deliberate effort on the part of man to master a technique of fish raising which will yield results far superior to nature's." He believed that the pisciculturalists of the later nineteenth century could not "dispel the fallacy that fish culture need only consist of efficiently hatching all the eggs which can be obtained".[36] This commentator made no reference whatsoever to Maitland's work at a fishery whose "principal object" was "to improve the various breeds of salmonidae by careful selection".[37]

Yet, thanks to Maitland, all serious British pisciculturalists from the 1880s, and belatedly the Americans from the 1920s, were practising such techniques. Perhaps the principal reason for Maitland's disappearance from history is the obvious one – pisciculture is a topic which has never commanded detailed attention from historians. It does not rank alongside cotton and iron in the history of British business and industry and is not the kind of subject that one would expect most great Victorians to be remembered for. Yet Maitland's importance does not even feature in the piscicultural histories that *have* been written or in the many modern textbooks on aquaculture which begin with brief histories of the science. This seems to be largely because the literature that does exist is largely of North American origin and ignores the British contribution in much the same fashion as Maitland's work appears to have been ignored in the United States whilst he lived. The literature displays what the *Field*, not without irony, once saw as "the least soupcon of desire to exalt the doings of the American fish culturalists, and to look down upon the feeble efforts put forth in this insignificant part of the world, which might as well have been omitted".[38]

Another factor in Maitland's drift out of the limelight, however, must have been his own actions. Maitland largely retreated from piscicultural work after 1886, turning more to county politics. But, even before then, he had resented any idea of the fishery becoming some form of a tourist attraction, open to all and not just the pisciculturally-minded. He does not appear to have had either the time or the inclination to become a piscicultural hero and preferred that most people be kept "very much in the dark ... [knowing] ... nothing of the immense advance" that Howietoun had made in fish culture, in order to prevent the fishery being besieged by inquisitive journalists and other visitors.[39] As he told a fishery correspondent of *The Times* in 1894, "I am sorry but my rule is absolute to supply no information for press purposes. Good wine needs no bush."[40] The select few visitors that were admitted to the fishery did not usually get to meet Maitland personally since he gave "strict orders that

no one is to be shown over the ponds except during his absence".[41] Indeed, Maitland had realised the problems inherent in admitting visitors:
Never show fish to visitors, at least not without taking extraordinary precautions. One never knows what harm they may unwittingly do: They may move a sluice, or open a valve, or poke a stick through a fine screen, or feed the wrong fish, or frighten the tame ones till they refuse to come for their meals.[42]

Scotland has always been credited with having the best salmon and trout fisheries in the world and it is perhaps appropriate that it should also have provided the man who laid the basis for these fish to be farmed intensively in the twentieth century, being bred and improved in much the same fashion as livestock. Maitland's work clearly laid all the essential principles for the development of salmonoid culture. He had laid at Howietoun, as one of his contemporaries noted, "a foundation on which may be built a piscicultural edifice of commanding proportions, capable of doing great work".[43] Maitland did not single-handedly 'invent' modern pisciculture. His advances were more variations on a theme that had been established since the days of the Ancient Chinese and been further developed in the eighteenth century, than a completely new way of doing things. But surely science and the modern world owe as much, if not more, to those who apply and develop a discovery as to the inventors. The nature of the subject – pisciculture not being a mainstream field for historical study – means that the achievements of this man of the Forth have largely gone unrecognised. But if pisciculture were to rank alongside cotton and iron in economic history, Maitland himself would surely deserve a place equal to that of Kay, Hargreaves, Newcomen and Watt. As his obituarist in *The Times*, Henry Ffennell, hoped:
I think, Sir, as the founder and director of, perhaps, the finest fish hatchery in the world; an establishment which, I venture to assert, would do credit to a well-subsidised government department, the good work performed by the late Sir James Maitland at Howietoun should receive every recognition and should not be forgotten.[44]

References

1 Ling, S.W. *Aquaculture in Southeast Asia: An Historical Overview* 1977 pp.4-7. Royal Dublin Society 'A New Method of Breeding Salmon and Trout' and *Transactions of the Royal Dublin Society* 1 1800 p.119.
2 House of Commons Agriculture Committee, *Fourth Report - Fish Farming in the United Kingdom: Vol. 2; Minutes of Evidence and Appendices* 1990 pp.1-3 and Landau, M. *Introduction to Aquaculture* 1992 p.3.
3 *Field* 13 March 1886 p.319.
4 University of Stirling, HF/V47(i): Letter Book 1, p.59. Maitland to Livingstone Stone of the United States Commission on Fish and Fisheries, 13 Nov. 1880.
5 Barker-Duncan, J. 'Salmon and Trout Hatcheries in Scotland' *Third Annual Report of the Fishery Board for Scotland* 1884 pp.174-184.
6 University of Stirling, HF/V49: Letter Book 5, p.394. Maitland to R.B. Marston, (Editor) *Fishing Gazette*, 20 Feb. 1886.

7   *Fishing Gazette* 5 Nov. 1887 p.286.
8   Central Region Archives, FA1/6/1, p.236. *Falkirk Water and Drainage Bill* 1886. Minutes of evidence.
9   *The Times* 17 April 1882 p.6 and *Fishing Gazette* 13 Nov. 1897 p.355.
10 University of Stirling, HF/V48(i): Letter Book 3, p.271. Maitland to the Secretary of the 1883 London Fisheries Exhibition, 18 Oct. 1883.
11 University of Stirling, HF/V49: Letter Book 5, p.394. Maitland to R.B. Marston, (Editor) *Fishing Gazette*, 20 Feb. 1886.
12 Borodine, V 'Statistical Overview of Fish Culture in Europe and North America' *Transactions of the American Fisheries Society* 22 1893 p.108.
13 *The Times* 1 May 1886 p.6.
14 *Field* 17 April 1875 pp.381-2.
15 *Stirling Saturday Observer* 22 April 1882 p.3.
16 *Field* 9 Dec. 1882 p.836.
17 Maitland, J.R.G. *History of Howietoun* 1886 p.219.
18 Ibid. p.28 and Day, F. *British and Irish Salmonidae* 1887 p.267.
19 Maitland, J.R.G. *History of Howietoun* 1886 p.86.
20 *Field* 22 April 1882 pp.525-526.
21 Maitland, J.R.G. *History of Howietoun* 1886 p.12.
22 Day, F. *Fish Culture* 1883 p.16. Day, F. *British and Irish* p.208.
23 Ibid. p.227 and Day, F. 'The British Salmonidae' *Journal of the National Fish Culture Association* 1887 pp.3-26.
24 University of Stirling, HF/V51: Letter Book 7, p.621. James Guy, Fishery Secretary, to Messrs Handy of Alnwick, 25 April 1888.
25 *Field* 22 April 1882 pp.525-526.
26 Ewart, J. 'Report on the Progress of Fish Culture in America.' In *Third Annual Report of the Fishery Board for Scotland* 1884 p.90.
27 Sykes, A. 'Inbreeding Pond Reared Trout' *Transactions of the American Fisheries Society* 31 1902 pp.116-121. Emphasis my own. It is not known from where Sykes took Maitland's statement.
28 Hayford, C. and Embody, C. 'Further Progress in the Selective Breeding of Brook Trout at the New Jersey State Hatchery' *Transactions of the American Fisheries Society* 60 1930 pp.109-113.
29 Davis, H.S. 'Fish Cultural Developments in Recent Years' *Transactions of the American Fisheries Society* 68 1938 pp.234-239.
30 *Land and Water* 20 Nov. 1897 p.810 and *Field* 13 Nov. 1897 p.773.
31 *Stirling Saturday Observer* 21 Nov. 1897 p.4.
32 Clements, J. *Salmon at the Antipodes: A History and Review of Trout, Salmon and Char Introduced in Australasia* 1988 p.130.
33 Deacon, M. 'State Support for Useful Science: The Scientific Investigations of the Fishery Board for Scotland, 1883-1899.' In Scheiber, H.N. (ed.) *Ocean Resources: Industries and Rivalries Since 1800* 1990 p.1.
34 Munro, A.L.S. and Waddell, I.F. 'Growth of Salmon and Trout Farming in Scotland.' In Bailey, R.S. and Parrish, B.B. (eds.) *Developments in Fisheries Research in Scotland* 1987 p.246.
35 Laird, L. and Needham, T. *Salmon and Trout Farming* 1991 p.22.
36 Fish, F.F. 'Founders of Fish Culture: European Origins' *Progressive Fish Culturalist* 16 1936 p.8.
37 University of Stirling, HF/V50: Letter Book 6, p.92. Guy to Mr C. Proctor, Honorary Secretary of the Yorkshire District Fishery Board, 16 Nov. 1886.
38 *The Field* 11 March 1882 p.326.

39 *Stirling Saturday Observer* 28 Feb. 1880 p.1.
40 University of Stirling, HF/V57: Letter Book 13, p.117. Maitland to Henry Ffennell, 22 Jan. 1894. Maitland has taken this expression from Shakespeare's *As You Like It.*
41 University of Stirling, HF/V47(i): Letter Book 1, p.400. Guy to Mr Anderson of Bridge of Allan, 11 April 1881.
42 Maitland, J.R.G. *History of Howietoun* 1886 p.101.
43 Bertram, J.G. 'Pisciculture – Its Progress and Utility' *Blackwoods Magazine* 131 1882) p.606.
44 *The Times* 19 Nov. 1897 p.6. Howietoun did not die with Maitland but has continued in operation. It is now owned by the University of Stirling and operates both as a fish farm and as a research station for the University's Institute of Aquaculture.

Sir James Maitland

BOOK REVIEWS (Naturalist)

Scottish Woodland History. Smout, T.C. Editor. Scottish Cultural Press, Edinburgh. ISBN 1-898218-53-6. £9.99.

This fascinating book had its origins at a conference on Scottish woodland history in 1995 and shows the many recent advances which have been made in the understanding of our woodlands.

It has fifteen chapters. The first chapter is on land-use history and makes an important point on the reliability of Blaeu's copied maps of 1654 and the need to consult the less accessible originals of 1585-1596 which were drawn by Timothy Pont. Chapters 2-6 show five different approaches to understanding old Scottish woodlands and include an investigation (by Breeze) of the original Roman sources of the belief (largely ill-founded) of the Great Wood of Caledon and another on Glasgow's old oaks (by Dougall and Dickson). The remaining nine chapters deal with the exploitation of semi-natural woodland. There are introductory chapters (by Smout) on this exploitation from 1600-1800 and on woodland management as seen through the Baron's Court records (by Watson). The rest of the chapters are woodland history case studies ranging from the Borders, through Highland Perthshire, to as far north as Assynt in Sutherland.

This is a very good book and shows the array of approaches and considerations that are essential if we are to understand the history, present-day ecology, and options for the future of our woodlands. None of the case studies were made close to Stirling and it behoves the readers of this journal to extend the in-depth investigation of local woodlands which has just begun (e.g. Wallis 1994). Scottish Woodland History must be essential reading for any naturalist who is interested in Scottish woodlands.

Reference

Wallis, J. (1994). *An Investigation into the Biological, Cultural and Conservation Significance of Myreton Wood.* Unpublished MSc thesis, University of Stirling.

J. Proctor

Robert Burns: a Man of All Seasons. John Young. Scottish Cultural Press. 250pp. ISBN 1-898218-60-9. £14.95.

The natural world of Robert Burns: quotations, notes, indexes ... of the poet on flowers, animals, trees, birds, landscapes ... a thoroughly researched work about the nature knowledgeable bard, by an SNH naturalist of today. A 'sampling' was offered for publication to FNH, and commented on, some years ago: now well produced by SCP, with commending foreword by a naturalist and past President of the Burns Federation, Wilson Ogilvie.

BETWEEN CARRON AND AVON: THE GRANGEMOUTH AREA SINCE 1600

J. G. Harrison

Introduction

Writing in 1723, Johnstoun of Kirkland described the view north from Falkirk. The Carron was a meandering, tidal river whilst the fertile carse was one of the pleasantest views in Scotland[1]. That vista today is dominated by Grangemouth with its modern industries. This paper presents a study of that area since about 1600. It concentrates on the coastal zone from the mouth of the Carron to the Avon, from Heuk to Bearcrofts on Plan 2. But, to put change there into context, it will necessarily look further afield. A detailed study of the agricultural scene familiar to Johnstoun is followed by a less detailed examination of the progress of industrialisation, the early growth of Grangemouth and the most recent transformations brought about by large-scale modern industries[2].

Sea Walls and Flood Defences in the Pre-Industrial Era

Roy's map (Plan 1) shows the area as surveyed in the mid 18th century. The Carron, Avon and Grange Burn are all tidal and meandering, much wider than today. The Carron enters the Forth about 1 km north of its present mouth. There is a string of farms between the mouths of Carron and Avon and, between those farms and the Forth, Roy shows a double line with sharp angles

Plan 1. Roy's map shows the area in the mid 18th century.

and turns, clearly intended to indicate a sea wall. The Kinneil shoreline is an equally unnatural smooth, crescentic sweep.

There is evidence for extensive embankment along the tidal Forth and its tributaries in the 17th century. The late 18th century Old Statistical Account refers to a sea wall of unknown antiquity at Ferriton, below Clackmannan[3]. The manuscript version of Roy's map (not illustrated) shows a sea wall in that area, similar to the one between Carron and Avon. A tack* of 1636 obliged the tenants of Ferriton to concur in

Repayrying and re-edifieing of the hale sea dykes demolished be Invadations of Watter and sall menteyne the same in as gud estait as they have bene thay yeris bypast[4].

Sibbald mentions dykes in discussing of the area 'betwixt the Water of Carron & Avon' but may only refer to dykes on the lesser rivers. In 1667, the Justices of the Peace for Stirlingshire determined to build dykes to prevent the sea spoiling the highways below Falkirk – though it is not clear if anything was done[5]. There is archaeological evidence of 17th century reclamation from the sea at Airth. A tack for a notably long 42 years at Airth and dated 1696 required the tenant to maintain the sea walls – without saying that these were either new or old. Duncan Johnstone, who farmed at Foulerhaich of Ebbishaugh, Falkirk parish and died about 1643, owed rent for 'fodder foulzie in sie dykis'. John Callander's 1662 tack of West Kerse obliged him to maintain the old sea dykes and replace them if needed. A disposition of 1744 refers to the Water Dykelands of Heuk and 6 acres of Saltcoats surrounded with a water-dyke. In a 1760 tack for Powdrake the landlord engaged to provide stones which the tenant was to cart and use 'to defend the sea-dykes'. And at Kinneil a 1697 tack required the tenant 'to keep the tide thereoff'[6].

So, it seems that sea dykes were widespread along the 17th century Forth. At Airth, mud flats had been reclaimed; elsewhere, sea walls may have been built on salt marsh, reclaiming arable land to landward. There is no evidence of when or how they were first built. Sibbald and the Clackmannan OSA emphasise their fragility and this is underscored by the need for repairs by the tenants though the 1760 record of re-enforcement with stones may represent real change. Sea walls were troublesome, expensive and unusual. Did they protect a particularly valuable agricultural area?

Agriculture from 1600 to 1720

Traditional accounts of Scotland's agricultural development emphasised the importance of the so-called Agricultural Revolution of the late 18th and early 19th century. Farming, it was argued, was rapidly transformed from a backward, near static peasant subsistence into a modern market-oriented and highly productive endeavour. One of the novel features of that 'revolution' was extensive reclamation of arable from muir, marsh or sea. A more nuanced view now prevails. Whilst the rate and scale of change in the late 18th and early

---

*Tack: lease.

19th century was impressive and brought about unprecedented increases in production, change emerged from a situation which was more varied, more progressive and often more productive than was earlier thought[7].

Failing a good run of estate papers, the Stirlingshire Sheriff Register of Deeds yielded a modest selection of tacks and the testaments of local farmers provided a wealth of detailed information (Plan 2)[8].

Many 17th century testaments provide a comprehensive list of assets and liabilities at the time of death. Unlike leases and rentals, which state what ought to happen, the testament indicates what did happen. However, they survive only for a minority of people and provide only a snapshot view of a particular moment – which may not be typical of an entire life. They do not record 'real estate' such as land and houses, but only 'moveable' property. But for agricultural tenants 'movables' included farm stock – both animals and crops; leases and rentals rarely mention livestock in arable areas. But, for technical, legal reasons testaments may not record all the movables and after the end of the 17th century, local testaments rarely include useful agricultural information. Nonetheless, from around 1620 to around 1690, they are invaluable.

Individual testaments can provide a cornucopia of illuminating detail. Bearcrofts was a large farm just north of the Avon occupied by a succession of substantial tenants. Thomas Boog's wife died there in February 1639 when,

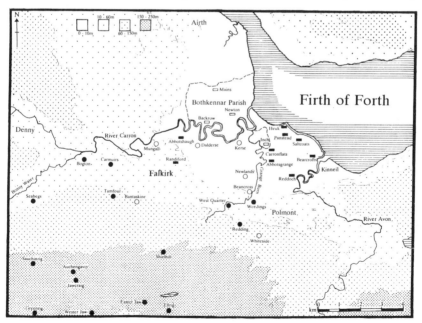

Plan 2. Some farm sites in the Grangemouth area 1600-1750.

Boog declared, the couple had the following livestock: 11 horses and mares, worth £20 Scots* each; 2 one year old foals, worth £8 each; 6 oxen, worth £20 each; 6 in-calf cows, worth £12 each; 4 stots, two years old, worth £6 13s 4d each; 6 stots, one year old, worth £4 each; 43 sheep, young and old, worth £2 each.

The adult horses and oxen were draught animals and they had 17 at a time when few farms elsewhere had more than two or three horses and one or two oxen; this was their motive power, assistance with the drudgery of working the land without machines. The foals are potential replacements or might be sold once they were older. The year-old stots are last year's calves. Two-year old stots are more valuable than one-year olds but still not nearly so valuable as adult, in-calf cows. In the spring, lambs would augment the sizeable flock of sheep and the cows would calve.

In the barn and barnyard they also had: 40 bolls* of bere* barley, threshed and unthreshed, worth £226; 136 bolls beans, threshed and unthreshed, worth £634; 26 bolls white oats, price illegible; 64 bolls outfield oats, price illegible. And they had utensils worth a humble £26. As the total value of this inventory was £1910 we can calculate that, between them, the white and outfield oats were worth £553, averaging just over £6 the boll. This was probably not their full production for the previous year. By February, some would have been consumed, sold or otherwise disposed of. But clearly grains (valued at £1393) overshadow the value of the livestock at £566. White oats was a high-yielding variety, requiring good soil, heavy manuring and a mild climate; the presence of outfield oats implies that some of the land was not sown to arable every year but was cropped only intermittently. The most striking feature of the grain stock is the presence of a large quantity of beans, approaching half the total grain recorded. To complete the couple's assets, they were owed a substantial £400.

But there were also liabilities. First, the rent for the previous year 'for the half lands of Bearcrofts', was £433 cash with 30½ bolls of bere barley and 330 bolls of beans. Sale of most of the rest of the beans would just cover the cash portion of the rent, though completing the threshing would involve costs. And they owed another £666 to other people. At the end of the balancing operation, they had £373 to call their own.

Taking a wider view, testaments suggest that there were four agricultural zones in the Falkirk area in the 17th century. In the southern and western parts, which we will call Zone 1, peas and beans are not mentioned in a sample of 44 testaments from 15 sites. Typically, these farms had ten times more oats than bere and sometimes the ratio was even higher. Jonet MacAndrew, who died at Wester Jaw about 1667, had 20 bolls oats and only one of bere, whilst Jeills Leishman, who died at Elrig in 1661, had sown 5 bolls of oats and only

---

*£ Scots: in the 17thC £1 Sterling was £12 Scots.
*Boll: grain measure of about 50 kg.
*Bere: a hardy form of barley.

half a boll of bere, expecting a two fold return on oats and three-fold on bere. And, again typical for Zone 1, each of these had only one horse. George Russell in Wester Jaw died in 1665 and had the largest quantities of grains recorded from this zone, 50 bolls oats and 50 bolls bere barley – he also had 3 horses and mares and 8 cows with some young stock. But he does not seem to have grown legumes.

Individually, these testaments might be only partial listings or might be unrepresentative; but in aggregate they tell such a consistent tale that it must describe the usual modes of farming in Zone 1. There was no white oats here but hardier, less demanding and less productive varieties called brockit oats, outfield oats, gray oats or black muirland oats. Quantities sown were small; returns were never estimated at above three to one and were more often only two to one. Unpaid wages, listed amongst the liabilities, indicate that these farms rarely employed as many as three paid workers. Rents were sometimes as low as £25 per year and seldom more than £60; they were payable in cash without any grain component. We have no positive local evidence about how rotations were organised; probably the bere barley got most of the manure, whilst land exhausted by the serial growing of oats would then be left for several years till it recovered.

This pattern is typical of more traditional mixed farming areas and approaches the pattern once thought to be typical of almost all 17th century Scotland. Much of the grain would be used on the farm, for human and animal feed, though a surplus might be sold in good years. Other products would include meat, wool, milk, butter and cheese. From time to time surplus stock would be sold. Overall productivity was low. Doubtless some supplemented farming with other work, for example mining, quarrying, spinning and weaving, all recorded from this area.

Zone 2 agriculture was found (roughly) between the fertile northern fringe of the area and the poorer ground to the south and west. Five of the farms were on the carselands, two on the lower hills. At two sites, Whiteside (Whyte, 1631 and Stirling, 1664) and Bantaskine (Marshall, 1668) some testaments were of Zone 1 type. But James Mitchell at Whiteside had two stacks of brockit oats, 32 bolls of oats, one stack of white oats, a stack of bere barley and two 'racks' of peas. Peas formed only a tiny part of his production. But he owed a substantial rent, including £100 cash with 16 bolls bere and 8 bolls oatmeal; and he grew some white oats, the variety typical of better land.

Seven sites, covered by 31 testaments, were assigned to Zone 2. Farms were assigned to this zone if legumes were sometimes present but usually at less than 20 % of production; the proportion was often considerably less than this. At Dalderse, one case where they form 22 % of production must be set against several others from this small estate where they form under 10 %. White oats were often recorded but outfield oats was usually the most important single crop and black oats appears on one occasion, at Kerse in 1639. The ratio of oats to bere was generally narrower than in Zone 1, usually between 2:1 and 5:1. Numbers of draught animals were higher here than in Zone 1.

Zone 3 was concentrated along the coast between Carron and Avon with outliers inland at Randiford and Abbotshaugh. Thirty-five testaments provided usable information derived from 9 sites. The size of holdings varied and not all testaments provide equal detail. But the Boog/Baird testament was typical in the emphasis on arable and in the importance of legumes. William Boog, the couple's son, died 12 years later; he and his father were both tenants in Bearcrofts. William was a married man with a young son. He and his wife had owned eight horses, two oxen and five cows with their calves. In the spring before he died they had sown 78 bolls of white oats, from which a three-fold return was anticipated, seven bolls bere barley, for which a four-fold return was forecast, 24 bolls outfield oats, promising only a two-fold return and 24 bolls beans, expected to yield three-fold.

All but two of the testaments from this zone show 20 % or more of the grain sown or harvested to be beans and/or peas. Returns of two to one are recorded for outfield oats, which was sometimes, even here, the largest single crop; but threefold returns were otherwise usual and bere barley sometimes produced a fourfold return. White oats was widely grown and, on these farms, gray and black oats were never recorded. Most had from four to eight adult horses and two oxen but, as we have seen, some had more draught animals than this whilst smaller farms (indicated by smaller rents and lower quantities of planting) obviously had fewer. Young stock and sheep are recorded from almost all sites. Many Zone 3 lists enumerate from five to eight farm servants, both men and women, some owed harvest wages but most full-time workers owed six months or a year's wages. If we assume the tenant family to comprise a conservative average of two adults and two children, some of these farms were supporting as many as a dozen people.

The most sophisticated agriculture was to be found in Bothkennar parish (Zone 4). Thirteen testaments from Bothkennar cannot be localised to a specific site; only two of these do not mention legumes as a significant part of the produce. Twelve derive from defined areas of the parish with two from Backraw, four from Mains and six from Newton; all these include peas and beans as 20 % or more of total production. But, in addition, many Bothkennar testaments record wheat crops, which had been grown here from as early as the 14th century. It was a luxury, sold to make wheat bread[9].

Peas and beans were grown to maturity, dried and sold as food for a growing urban population unable to afford animal protein. They imply the use of lime to reduce the acidity of the soil with the further benefit of making heavy clay soils easier to work. And whilst the mechanisms were not understood it was known that both liming and legumes increased the yield of subsequent crops. Lime also assists to remove salt from land reclaimed from the sea. We have seen that legumes were present. What of liming? For direct evidence we must turn to tacks – which also yield other valuable information.

The Sheriff Register of Deeds (checked to 1725) yielded some 30 tacks from the Falkirk area dated from 1661 to 1721. Only three are from Zone 1 with two from Redding (1699 and 1708), one from Jawcraig (1722). They are consistent with the pattern of small farms with modest cash rents deduced from the testamentary evidence. The farms were on 19 year leases, as was usual in Stirlingshire by this time; this was long enough for tenants to invest in the long-term future of their farm and at Jawcraig in 1718 the tenant was required to apply 10 bags of lime per year to the arable and only to grow crops on the outfield for three years in a row and then to leave it fallow for a further three. The landlord agreed to pay for the last two years' lime. At Redding in 1708 the tenant was to supply 30 bags of lime per year to his landlord as part of his rent, doubtless from a lime quarry on his land. Presumably he applied lime to his own land. Perhaps, even in Zone 1, we are here picking up the first signs of 'improvement'.

The tacks from Zones 2 to 4 will be considered together. They range from 1661 (at Heuk) to 1720 (at Little Fold of Dalderse). They were usually for 19 years, a few specifying that the lease was renewable for two or even three 19-year terms. Several specify that the landlord will provide assistance with the building of a new house at the beginning of the lease – some were houses of stone and lime, another sign of 'improvement'. All require the tenants to muck and till the ground adequately. Several specify that tenants are not to grow oats twice in a row on the same ground; this was a common prohibition and, surprisingly given the evidence of the testaments, was the only direct reference to crop rotation. Perhaps, where rotation was a well-established tradition, it was simply assumed rather than specified. The payment of rents in diverse grains in specified proportions also forced tenants to rotate. We might assume rotation of bere/ oats/ legumes on the infield of Zone 3 with wheat/ bere/ oats/ legumes in Bothkennar.

Five of the carseland tacks specify that the landlord will supply or pay for lime to be applied to the land, usually at the beginning of the lease. These are all from Zone 2, three from Dalderse (1717a, 1717b, and 1720), one from Kerse (1714) and one from Merryflats (1696). At Dalderse the landlord granted a cash discount from rents for the first two or three years to cover part of the cost of limestone to be laid on the land; at Kerse and Merryflats, the specification is for boats of limestone.

In 1696 Thomas Johnstone and his son took over one oxgate of land at Merryflats; a new house was to be built on it, their rent was 13 bolls oatmeal, 13 bolls bere for five years rising to 14½ bolls each thereafter with some additional straw, poultry etc; and, for the first two years, they were to buy and lay on the land four boatfuls of limestone, the price of one boatful being deducted from the rent. In 1714, in a tack, which obliged the tenant to pay part of his rent in peas, Hope of Kerse agreed to supply a boatful of lime worth £20 for each of the first three years of the tack at Kerse, the tenant agreeing to lay it on.

There were lime workings in the upland parts of Falkirk and Polmont parishes in the 17th century but these carseland farms clearly relied on 'boat lime' from workings on the south side of the Forth, available since at least the 14th century[10]. Limestone was calcined in kilns with coal; coal was mined in the Heuk, Saltcoats and Pansteads area till about the 1630s and was being mined at Quarrelshore (on the Carron) in the later 17th century, if not before. The Carron (and probably the Grange Burn) could be used to transport lime and coal to landward parts of the carse whilst boats which brought lime in could take coal out as a return cargo.

There was, thus, a broad and unsurprising difference between the 'traditional' farming of the upland area and the more progressive, market-orientated farming of the low ground. Liming and legumes were key elements in this progressive agriculture. There was a transitional area between. The evidence cautions against interpreting this as merely a reflection of 'natural' productivity. Altitude, rainfall and poor soil limited productivity of the upland areas but small holdings and lack of capital were also significant. In the later 18th century productivity was vastly increased over much of this upland zone using more advanced methods – and we have seen some signs of this in the form of liming and fallowing even in the early 18th century.

On the low ground, liming, sophisticated cropping and the deployment of large numbers of draught animals were human interventions, the investment protected by expensive sea walls. Estate management was a significant variable. Many farmers in Bothkennar were obliged to grow wheat to fulfill the demands of a Crown charter whilst the Kerse Estate (owners of Kerse itself, Newlands, Beancross and Dalderse) seem to have been less exacting and progressive than owners to the north and west, at least till the early 18th century when evidence for liming appears in the Kerse tacks just quoted. It is likely that Zone 2 generally was advancing towards Zone 3 methods by the early 18th century.

Transport and markets were also vital elements for the more advanced areas. Liming depended on riverine transport. Some grain may have been shipped out directly from the farms. Tacks provide direct evidence of the importance of markets, specifying that grain paid as rent on the low ground was to be carted to markets at Falkirk, Stirling and even Kilsyth. Many tenants in the fertile lowland areas also had business and family contacts in Falkirk, Bo'ness and Linlithgow, where they may have sold some of their own grains. Preliminary investigation suggests that a similar zone of market-orientated, high productivity involving legumes, lime and numerous draught animals was established by the early 17th century north and south of the Forth almost so far up-stream as Stirling. The Grangemouth area in the 17th century was thus part of fertile fringe, focused on the Forth and dependent on it for transport of supplies and produce and protected from its floods by expensive sea walls.

The Early Industrial Period

Pivotal to the future economic growth of the area was the canalisation, re-direction and embankment of the Carron (1768 to 1785) to facilitate access to the Carron Company's wharves at Carronshore. Even more significant was the construction of the Forth-Clyde canal. The initial eastern terminal was a tidal harbour at the widened and deepened mouth of the Grange Burn (Plan 3). The

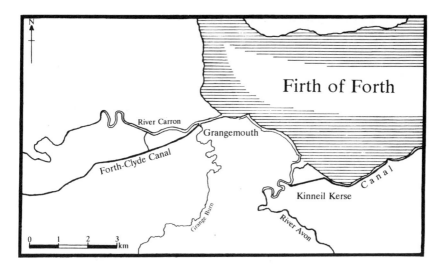

Plan 3. Canalization – in the later 18th century.

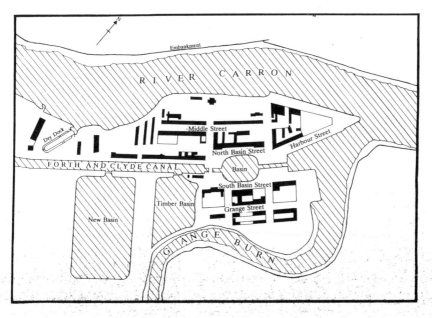

Plan 4. Grangemouth in the early 19th century.

canal reached Kirkintillock by 1773 whilst a cut provided access to Carron Works by 1775; long before the through route opened to the west coast in 1790 a town had begun to develop at the eastern terminus, on the narrow neck of land between the Carron and the canal. Here a mix of residential and business premises accommodated a community, which serviced the canal, and the docks where some goods were trans-shipped. In its early days this town was known as Sea Lock but, well before the end of the century, it had been re-named Grangemouth[11].

A canal spur from Bo'ness, across Kinneil Kerse and by a viaduct across the Avon was begun but abandoned due to financial problems and a short section of this aborted canal lies within BP's Kinneil site. The older ports of Bo'ness and to a lesser degree Alloa were now eclipsed by Grangemouth and during the next few decades rapid expansion of the Grangemouth/Falkirk area was mainly driven by exploitation of coal and ironstone and its strategic position on increasingly important internal and international routes[12].

The initial site of Grangemouth was full by about 1800 when expansion moved south of the Grange Burn. Establishment of a customs house (1810), building of a graving dock on the Carron (1811), a link via the Union Canal to Edinburgh (1822) and the establishment of industries secondary to the docks (e.g. sawmills, rope and sail manufacture) all demanded space, put pressure on existing dock facilities and employed more labour (Plan 4). Steam ships were

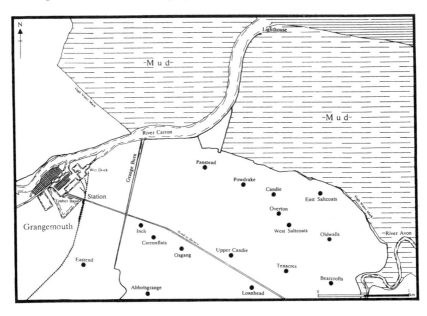

Plan 5. By 1860 the landscape was being transformed.
Note the railway and re-aligned Grange Burn.

deployed on the Forth from 1813 and vessels now became ever larger. The old, tidal harbour on the Grange Burn became manifestly inadequate and a new deep-water dock was constructed. Development of the town moved south of the Grange Burn, which was later re-aligned, outside the urban area (Plan 5).

Some of these changes had a direct impact on local farms. At Dalderse the canal divided fields from their steadings but a bridge was built, the old sea-dykes were replaced and tenants allowed to use the canal to bring in limestone and coal in compensation. By 1760 the tenants of Saltcoats were granted liberty to bring in lime and coal via the new docks at Carronshore. But the canal and Carron Works were themselves indicative of a new commercialism, which had less direct effects. Powdrake was newly divided by march ditches around 1760, a new house and steading was built for the tenants and liming was specified in the tack. A scatter of similar evidence has been found for change starting to accelerate around 1760 not just in the Falkirk area but throughout Stirlingshire[13]. Wilson comments on the dramatic changes around Falkirk in the 40 years to 1794 but regarded the previous 14 years as those of the most dramatic transition, detailing the changes on the Callendar estates during those years. He recognised three main agricultural zones in the area: the carse was the best land, there was also 'good land which is not of carse quality' and areas where 'the soil is poor, wet and spongy'[14]. The carse yielded good crops of grain and hay on a six-course rotation: fallow/wheat/beans and peas/barley/grass/oats. The few animals kept were either draught animals or for domestic milk production. Improved drainage and the availability of machinery were cited as the major factors in improvement.

By about 1840, there was significant loss of farmland to urban development whilst surviving farms were expanding by amalgamation[15]. As elsewhere, larger farms allowed increased capitalisation; contemporary commentators on the area emphasise the importance of iron ploughs, horse-driven threshing machines and more efficient drainage as well as 'improved' breeds of cattle and new strains of seeds in the early 19th century. By the 1840s liming and a six-course rotation were said to be universal on the carselands of east Stirlingshire[16].

From this period on, Estate Plans enrich our view of the farms. Particularly interesting is one of Kerse Estate in 1830 showing fields and the layout of individual farms, with ditches, gardens, orchards and ponds and a stone-faced sea wall. A plan of Bearcrofts in 1847 shows a substantial two-storey, four-roomed house with a dairy at the rear[17]. And from this period, too, the censuses open a new window onto the area. In 1851, Bearcrofts was inhabited by Robert Walker (farmer, aged 35, unmarried head of household), Mary Bow, dairymaid aged 49 and four other servants, two male, two female. Walker farmed 60 acres in all on a 19-year lease, requiring a six-course rotation[18]. The dairy and dairymaid mean more milk cows than was general on the carse - was the farm supplying Grangemouth with milk? James Chapman at Upper Candie in 1851 was another specialist, a market gardener with 8 acres, living with his wife and 7 children in three rooms whilst at Awalls there was an extended family; William Binnie, aged 65 and farmer of 52 acres, was the head of household and lived with his wife aged 67, their daughter, single aged 38, their granddaughter, single and 19 who was a dairymaid, another granddaughter aged 3, a nephew aged 38, single and a land steward and two men servants, a ploughman and a boy. Next door lived a ploughman, John Binnie (presumably their son), his wife, two children and their lodger, Thomas Nimmo aged 25. At Oldwalls there were now two households, one headed by a ploughman but the other by Alexander Frazer, engine smith, living alone in two rooms.

Grangemouth could not keep pace with its expanding population and some people – whether from choice or lack of it – worked in the town but lived in the countryside. There were a porter and a dock labourer at Pansteads, a wright and another dock labourer at Oxgang and so on. There may, of course, have been a counter-movement as some people living in the town came out to work on the farms, to milk the cows on a daily basis, perhaps, or for haymaking and harvest. Large scale, 1st Edition Ordnance Survey maps (surveyed 1860) show a network of paths connecting farms and town, attesting to their close links; each farm is shown with its garden and associated farm buildings. The Ordnance Survey Name Book indicates that all the steadings at this time were of one or two storeys, most were slated but a few were thatched or partially thatched. North Powdrake was in ruins but the others were in good repair.

Railways had proliferated in central Scotland since the 1840s but a line to Grangemouth was not built till 1860, taking over the canal's passenger traffic and most of the freight (Plan 5). The canal was now of minor importance but the port continued to expand. The Carron Dock was excavated in 1882, with direct railway access to the quays, speeding up cargo handling. The town centre now moved southward and the urban area itself continued to expand with streets of tightly packed tenements close to the docks and urban centre whilst rows of more spacious houses and villas marched across the carselands. Access to the port had, hitherto, been via the Carron; in 1906, construction of the Grange Dock allowed direct access from the deep water of the Forth (Plan 6).

This expansion of the urban and industrial area was largely at the expense of farmland but there was also some reclamation. The Grange Dock was a major encroachment onto the estuarine mud-flats; a triangle of land reclaimed from mud east of the expanded docks may have been an accidental result of work on the channel of the Carron and, on a lesser scale, Bearcrofts had gained around 5.6 acres of sea greens.

During the later 19th century potatoes and turnips appear as field crops even on carseland farms, probably pointing to a swing back towards the keeping of livestock. But there is very little information about rotations, Bearcrofts again providing an exception. A note of a lease current around 1895 indicated it now consisted of 119 acres; the rotation was one fallow grass, two wheat, one beans and barley and five gray oats whilst 6 acres of turnips were to be left at the end of the lease[19]. So legumes were still present though vastly reduced in importance.

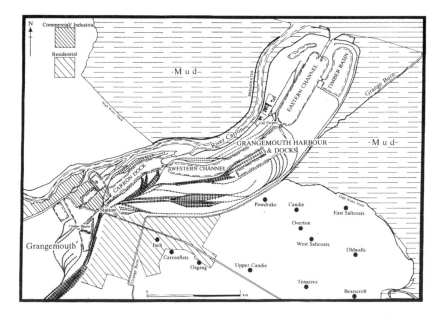

Plan 6. Late 19th century: the railway docks and expanding town.

Turning to the 1891 census we find that Bearcrofts is still a farm (Robert Meikle, living with wife, infant daughter, 1 female domestic and 2 male agricultural servants). Overton Farm was occupied by James Marshall, his wife, sister in law and a male farmworker. Powdrake was farmed by a new generation of the Inglis family; the couple had 8 children, the two oldest apparently helping with the farm, and 3 resident male farmworkers. At Upper Candie James Chapman still ran a market garden at age 69, helped by his unmarried adult son. South of Bo'ness Rd, Claret was still a farm but John English at Loanhead was a dairyman.

But there were no more farms. Oldwalls seems to be uninhabited, though the buildings were still standing. At Tenacres there were five houses, some presumably converted farm buildings. The heads of household, however, were 2 dock labourers, a railway carter, a ploughman and a brewer's lorryman whilst William Wilson's son was a general labourer, one daughter was a dairymaid and another a dressmaker. Overtown Cottages, a new building, housed 3 families, two headed by farmworkers, one by a dock labourer; at Awalls the heads of household are a ships plater, a tinsmith and a farm grieve or head man. At 'Old Saltcoats' was a seaman, at Saltcoats a general labourer, at Panstead a dock labourer. Some of these people had working children but few worked on the land. The total acreage of farmland lost to industry was still small; yet clearly it was industry and the port which now dominated the local economy.

Chemicals, Petro-chemicals and 20th century industry

By the early 20th century, Grangemouth was east central Scotland's major port. Main imports were timber and grain. Iron from the Carron Works and other foundries was an important export. During the 19th century chemicals (initially mainly derived from coal) joined this outward flow. James Young had developed his process for the fractional distillation of mineral oils in the mid 19th century, giving rise to the important shale oil industry. However, this soon faced competition from imports of crude oil, at first particularly from the US. As early as 1866 there was a 'massive' refinery in Stirling, processing crude imported from the US via the Forth-Clyde canal[20]. Oil storage facilities at Grangemouth Docks probably date from this period.

In the early 20th century, as the demand for oil products rose, the indigenous industry was in decline; the First World War gave it an artificial lease of life but termination of hostilities signaled the eventual supremacy of imported crude. Grangemouth had particular attractions for the new, large-scale, technical industries of the post-war world, including space for expansion, a good, cheap water supply, good communications by sea and rail, proximity to major cities and a town council eager to attract new industries. These had been potent attractions to Scottish Dyes Limited (later ICI) which arrived in Grangemouth in 1919. They were also important for Scottish Oils Limited (later BP), seeking a site for a Scottish refinery as part of a worldwide expansion. The naval base at Rosyth was a potential customer and, vitally

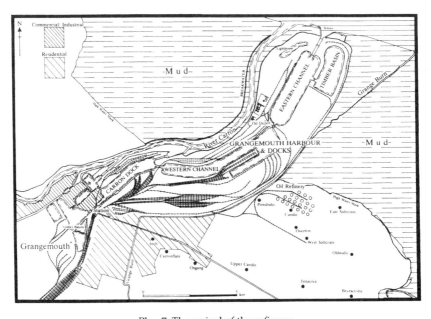

Plan 7. The arrival of the refinery.

important, the workforce and some of the hardware of the older industries (including a small refinery at Grangemouth) were available too.

Negotiations began with Grangemouth Town Council in 1921 and in 1924 the new plant was in productions, a berth for tankers up to 10,000 tonnes being opened at around the same time. To landward, the site was serviced by rail and road links and there was a pipeline link to the older Uphall refinery. Although the company bought all the land north of Bo'ness Road, only the northern end was developed at this stage with 10 tanks of 8,000 tonnes capacity, laboratory facilities and other support (Plan 7). The company built some housing for employees, mainly in the King's Road and Oswald Avenue areas[21].

During the inter-war years expansion was limited by the depression and was achieved within the existing refinery area. Grangemouth, too, grew only modestly during these years and work at the refinery was suspended at the outbreak of war in 1939, resuming in or shortly after 1945. It was not till 1952 that the new, expanded refinery opened, now occupying the whole land north of Bo'ness Road. Since 1952 changes in oil-based industries worldwide – from the massive increase in car use to the previously unimaginable diversity of products now derived from oil – have had an obvious impact on BP's Grangemouth operation. More specific to the local context have been the development of North Sea oil and gas industries and the options presented by the complex of related industries present in the Grangemouth area for joint ventures and the inter-change of products.

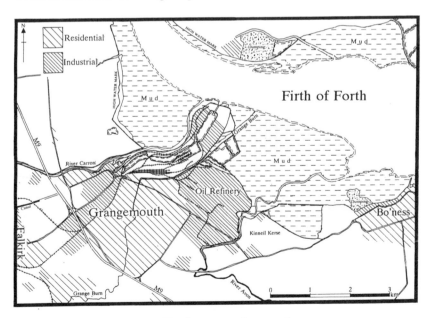

Plan 8. The Grangemouth area today.

Other industries were also expanding. From 1963 Grangemouth was designated a growth area, bringing favourable grants and loans for investors, assistance with finding industrial sites and other advantages. Almost 6,000 council houses were built in Grangemouth between 1919 and 1971, the population grew by almost 300 % including a massive 3,340 rise from 1951 to 1961, bringing it to 18,867 an expansion subsequently maintained by the acceptance of 'overspill' population from Glasgow and the traditional industrial areas of the west coast.

Housing and industrial expansion put pressure on space and two poorly documented reclamation schemes have been initiated in the last 50 years. Dumping refuse and spoil between Kinneil and Bo'ness, with the evident intention of reclamation, has been curtailed and has had the paradoxical effect of creating the Kinneil Lagoons, a prime feeding site for waders. Another scheme, south of Grangemouth Docks, has also been only partially completed. The BP complex has expanded to Kinneil and across Bo'ness Road and other industries have spread across the carse towards Falkirk. Meanwhile, pressure on space has been partially relieved by curtailing residential expansion assuming that a car-borne work force can travel some distance to work (Plan 8).

Acknowledgements

I am grateful for financial support for this work from BP Oil Grangemouth Refinery Ltd and for encouragement from Graham Hamilton.

Stephen Digney drew the plans under difficult circumstances and has my deepest gratitude.

Abbreviations for references and appendices: Scottish Record Office (SRO) SRO, Stirlingshire Sheriff Register of Deeds, SC67/49 series, Deeds: SRO, Register of Testaments for the Commissariot of Stirling, CC21/5 series, Testatments.

References

1. Johnstoun [Mr of Kirkland], 1723, Morwenside Parish, Falkirk, Bothkennar, Airth, Larbert and Dunipace. In Mitchell, A. (ed) (1906) *Geographical Collection Relating to Scotland made by Walter MacFarlane.*
2. Useful sources for the pre-industrial history of the area include: Bailey G. (1992). Along and Across the River Carron, *Calatria* 2, 49-84: Reid J. (1993). The Carselands of the Firth of Forth, *Calatria* 4, 1-31: Porteous R. (1967) Grangemouth's Ancient Heritage.
3. Roy, W. (1793). The Military Antiquities of the Romans in Britain: Moodie R. (1791), The Parish of Clackmannan. In The Statistical Account of Scotland IX (OSA) (Ed D.J. Witherington and I.R. Grant, 1978).
4. Scottish Record Office (SRO), Mar and Kellie Papers, GD124/17/203.
5. Sibbald, R. (1892). History and Description of Stirlingshire, p56: SRO Minutes of the Justices of the Peace for Stirlingshire, SC67/83/3 p. 8, May 1667.

6. Bailey, G. (1991). Excavations at Airth. *Forth Naturalist and Historian* 14, 111-120: SRO, Deeds, SC67/49/2 f. 90v: SRO, Testaments, CC21/5/5 f.183: Testaments, CC21/5/8 f. 240v; Deeds, SC67/49/17 p 296: Deeds, SC67/49/22 p. 291; Deeds, SC67/49/3 f. 38r.
7. Devine, T. (1994). The Transformation of Rural Scotland; Social Change and the Agrarian Economy 1660-1815: Whyte, I. (1979). Agriculture and Society in Seventeenth Century Scotland.
8. For testaments studied for this section see Appendix 1. For tacks see Appendix 2.
9. Payments of wheat from Bothkennar are recorded from the early 14th century: Exchequer Rolls of Scotland I, p.179, Edinburgh, 1878: Regesta Regum Scottorum; the acts of David II, p122, item 84, Edinburgh University Press, 1982.
10. Harrison, J.G. (1993). Lime Supply in the Stirling area from the 14th to the 18th centuries. *Forth Naturalist and Historian* 16, 83-89.
11. Russell, R. (1962). Lost Canals and Waterways of Britain, pp. 247-253: Porteous, R. (1970) Grangemouth's Modern History 1768-1968: Semple, D. (1958), The Growth of Grangemouth; a note. *Scottish Geographical Magazine* 74, 78-85: Hulley, AC. (1968). Historical and Geographical Background to the Survey. In Grangemouth/Falkirk Regional Survey & Plan, Scottish Development Department pp 17-24.
12. Hulley, A.C. (1968). Historical and Geographical Background to the Survey. In Grangemouth/Falkirk Regional Survey & Plan, Scottish Development Department p17.
13. SRO Deeds, SC67/49/22 p.291: SRO Deeds, SC67/49/24, p.4: SRO Deeds, SC67/49/27 p.208.
14. OSA Falkirk pp 296-303.
15. 'Falkirk' pp 14-17 in The New Statistical Account of Scotland VIII, 1841
16. SRO, Kerse Estate Rent Book 1840-1871, GD173/3/5.
17. SRO, Kerse Estate Plans, RHP4832 & RHP80017.
18. SRO, Kerse Estate Rent Book 1840-1871, GD173/3/5; this volume includes additional notes for later years.
19. SRO, Kerse Estate Rent Book 1840-1871, GD173/3/5; notes for 1895-6.
20. Stirling Observer 1st Oct 1866, p.5, col. 3-4: I am grateful to Alastair MacLaren for drawing this reference to my attention.
21. Falkirk Herald, 6th Jan 1923, p.7,col.3: Falkirk Herald, 26th Nov 1924: Ferrier, R.W. (1982). The History of the British Petroleum Company; I, The Developing Years 1901-1932, Cambridge University Press, pp. 466, 483: Grangemouth Town Council Minutes, from 1921- 1924 (particularly for the water supply), Falkirk: BP internal plan G/1067; copy kindly provided by G. Hamilton.

Appendices

Appendix 1: Tacks to 1725. Some testaments also include details about tacks.

Abbotsgrange
Tack dated 1719 by William Drummond to Robert Walker, SC67/49/8 f. 296.

Bantaskine
Tack dated 1718 by Mr Michael Livingstone to John Buchanan in Chapelyards of the lands of Chapelyards of Bantaskine, SC67/49/8, f. 218; by the same, dated 1721, to James Millar of Chapelyards of Bantaskine with pendicles, SC67/49/8 f. 302.

Beancorse
Tack dated 1720, by Henry Beg to Thomas Beg, mason at Beancorse, SC67/49/9 f. 161.

Dalderse
   Tack dated 1717 by Livingstone of Glentirran to Jean Monteith, relict of John Lorn of
   Yonderhaugh of Dalderse, SC67/49/9 f. 182: by the same dated 1717 to William
   Callander and William Crawford, equally, of the Cuttbottom, Littlefold, Pazerfold,
   East Side and other parts of Dalderse, SC67/49/9 f. 182: by the same, dated 1720, to
   Thomas Forsyth of Little Fold (and other parts, as above) of Dalderse, SC67/49/9 f. 179.

Heuk
   Tack dated 1661 by the Earl of Callander to John Kincaid of lands of Heuk and
   Oswalds Saltcoats, SC67/49/7 f. 4v.

Jawcraig
   Tack dated 1722 by James Kincaid to Jon Aitken of the New Dyke of Jaw Craig,
   SC67/49/9 f. 152.

Kerse Estate
   Tack dated 1692 by Hope of Kerse to Alexander Cunningham of land at West Kerse,
   SC67/49/4 f 151v: by the same, dated 1700, to James Lockhart and spouse of 3 oxgates
   of Wester Powflett of Kerse, SC67/49/4 f. 152v: by the same, dated 1711, to William
   Hardie, of 25 acres of Kerse, SC67/49/7 f 256: by the same, dated 1714, to William
   Hardie of the 25 acres of Kerse (above) at a higher rent but with addition of a new
   house and a boat of limestone yearly for three years, SC67/49/7, f 254: by the same,
   dated 1696, to Thomas Johnstone in Maryflats and Thomas, his son of one oxgate of
   Maryflatts, SC67/49/2 f 103r.

Randiford
   Tack dated 1684 by Menteith of Randiford to John Callander, of part of Randiford,
   SC67/49/6 f. 218r: by the same, dated 1684, to James Watt and spouse of part of
   Randiford, SC67/49/5 f. 37r: by the same, dated 1703, renewing the previous lease to
   James Watt, on payment of a 'great sum', SC67/49/5 f. 38v: by, the same, dated 1703,
   to John Callander, renewing the previous lease of parts of Randiford, SC67/49/6 f.
   217v.

Redding
   Tack dated 1708 by Patrick Bellenden of Parkend of Redding to William Learmont,
   SC67/49/7, f237: dated 1699, by Earl of Callander to James Burn of Blairs of Redding,
   SC67/49/4 f. 155.

Mains of Bothkenner.
   Tack dated 1683 by John Cowie, to John Logan; SC67/49/4 f 27v.

Newton of Bothkennar.
   Tack dated 1695 by Wm Bruce of Newton to Alexr Mitchell in Spout of lands of
   Tennoch and Wester Yard, parts of Newton, SC67/49/3 f. 45r.

Appendix 2: Testaments

All testaments are in the Scottish Record Office, Commissariot of Stirling records.
Testaments from rural Falkirk were included only if they were locatable at least to estate
level and contained significant agricultural information; later, many of these sites were
assigned to Polmont parish.

Falkirk Parish

Abbotsgrange
   Lillias Graham, 6th December 1661: John Watt, 14th July 1669: Agnes Smith, 5th May
   1674.

Abbotshaugh
James Gudlet, 27th Sept 1651: Bessie Callander, 17th March 1654: William Gibb, 21st March 1656: Janet Morrison, 10th March 1658: Margaret Pinkerton, 10th Jan 1668: Thomas Burn, 30th Oct 1671.

Auchingavin
John Gray, 22nd Feb 1656: William Callander, 31st July 1663: Margaret Gray, 18th Feb 1676.

Bantaskin
John Marshall, 3rd Jan 1668: Edward Callander, 6th Feb 1679.

Beancross
Alexander Johnstone, 23rd Aug 1661.

Bearcrofts
Patrick Gibb, 23rd June 1630: Christian Baird, 16th March 1639: William Boog, 4th Dec 1641: Agnes Boig, 4th Dec 1661: Bartholomew Morrison, 21st July 1671: Helen Wright, 6th April 1672.

Bogton
James McKie, 5th Dec 1612: Patrick Muirhead, 22nd April 1643: Robert Williamson, 5th Oct 1666: Euphan [Stephen in printed Commissary Index] Jervay, 13th July 1666: Alex Muirhead, elder, 13th May 1670 & 25th Jan 1671: James Muirhead, 8th Oct 1677.

Carmuirs
Jon Livingstone, 7th July 1621: Janet Gilespie, 14th March 1667: Margaret Williamson, 14th Aug 1663: Margaret Aitken, 2nd June 1664: Robert Bachop, 14th Mar 1667: Jean Miller, 5th May 1675: James Hill, 5th Oct 1675: Robert Leishman, 8th Oct 1677: James Leishman, 2nd Dec 1677: John Walker, 13th Nov 1691.

Carronflats
Isobel Kincaid, 21st Aug 1619.

Dalderse
John Galbraith, 15th July 1625: Margaret Kincaid, 27th March 1632: James Johnstone, 5th Nov 1636: Robert Callander, 18th April 1644: Jean Gudlet and Alexander Johnstone 13th Feb 1680.

Elrig
James Forrest, 24th June 1644: Jeals Leishman, 13th July 1664

Greenrig
Margaret Henderson, 2nd Aug 1634: Christian Muirhead, 4th April 1635: Janet Auchie, 28th Feb 1668

Heuk
John Kincaid, 8th March 1671: Alexander Lorne, 28th Feb 1673.

Jaw, Easter
Christian Johnston, 16th April 1662: Thomas Fleming, 12th Jan 1666.

Jawcraig
Grissall Russall, 26th Feb 1664: John Russall, 6th Jan 1665.

Jaw, Wester
Janet McAndrew, 1st Jan 1668: George Russell, 1st Jan 1668: Christian Forrest, 5th April 1671.

Kerse
John Sword, 8th Oct 1635:John Young, 20th Jan 1642: Marion Scott, 9th Sept 1643: Margaret Galbraith, 23rd August 1644: David Johnstone, 14th March 1656: John Hardie, 21st March 1656: William Callander,3rd Nov 1658: Christian Johnstone, 7th March 1662: Charles Lockhart, 17th Dec 1662: Alexander Monteith, 23rd Aug 1663: John Callander, 17th March 1671: Isobel Morison, 14th Feb 1673: John Callander, 3rd Sept 1673: Marion Callander, 8th Oct 1677.

Mungall
Helen Letham, 24th March 1665: John Johnstone, 11th Feb 1667: George Gilmuir, 25th June 1669: John Hardie, 8th Oct 1677.

Newlands
George Johnstone, 27th Jan 1671: James Sword, 27th Dec 1676.

Panstead
John Ronald, 7th July 1621.

Randiford
Alexander Walker, 16th Aug 1672: Elizabeth Scott, 30th April 1680.

Redding
John Blackburn, 28th Feb 1618: Isobel Carnock, 30th Oct 1656: John Heart, 5th May 1675.

Reddoch
Margaret Marshall, 5th Nov 1631: James Mungall, 26th August 1635: Mareon Bruce, 17th Aug 1639: Henry Boog 19th Aug 1643: Marion Crawford, 8th Feb 1664: Janet Wood, 8th Oct 1677: Henry Simpson, 8th Oct 1677: William Bruce, 11th Jan 1679.

Saltcoats
Jon Carslaw, 12th Feb 1635: Janet Menteith, 12th March 1640: Janet Logan, 3rd Nov 1654: Margaret Seller, 4th Oct 1661: Elizabeth Livingstone, 5th August 1681: Robert Gardiner and Helen Ramsay, 7th July 1703.

Sauchinrig
John Boyd, 7th March 1662.

Seabegs
Helen Marshall, 1st June 1668: William Gilmuir, 8th Oct 1669: Thomas Callander, 9th May 1678.

Shielhill
Jonat Russal, 29th March 1617.

Tamfour (=Thomastoun)
Andrew Simpson, 31st May 1676.

Weedings
Margaret Livingstone, 17th June 1612: James Whyte, 9th Dec 1615.

West Quarter
Robert Livingstone, 19th April 1615: Alexander Livingstone, 15th Aug 1627.

Whiteside
Thomas Whyte, 5th Nov 1631: James Stirling, 8th Jan 1664: James Mitchell, 24th June 1664.

Bothkennar Parish
Bothkennar was entirely rural and a more inclusive policy has been adopted than for Falkirk parish. Some testaments were included which could not be located nearer than parish level. These appear first:
John Kincaid, 10th July 1613: Alexander Muirhead, 17th Nov 1636: James Simpson, 25th April 1654: John Masterton, 22nd Aug 1654: John Adam, 3rd May 1662: Bessie Burn, 19th Aug, 1664: Janet Callander, 12th Aug 1668; Margaret Simpson, 15th May 1671; Margaret Burn, 9th July 1675: James Taylor, 19th May 1676; Thomas Adam, 11th Aug 1676: Patrick Syme, 4th April 1677: Alexander Simpson, 12th July 1678.

Backraw of Bothkennar
Alexander Burn, 10th July 1668: Janet Bad, 30th May 1671.

Inch
Robert Walker and Elizabeth Johnstone, 23rd July 1673.

Mains of Bothkennar
John Simpson, 5th May 1627: William Westwood, 5th May 1627: Marion Espline, 3rd March 1671: John Cowie, 8th Sept 1674.

Newton of Bothkennar
James Callander, 21st Jan 1632: Janet Simpson, 22nd Jan 1664: John Simpson, 1st June 1664: Janet Burn, 16th May 1672: Janet Wilson, 8th May 1673: John Leishman, 1st Feb 1679.

BOOK REVIEWS (Historical)

Local Past. Peter Joynson of Laraich. pri. print. 270pp. 1996. £17.50.

Contains 32 selections of Aberfoyle area history, anecdote, legend, by a member of a prominent family. They include – Aberfoyle 3000 years ago; Hunting in Menteith; Ledourd; Flanders Moss; Cranogs; Kirk of Aberfoyle; the Joynsons and other Loch Ard families; Wartime Aberfoyle. This rich local lore is supplemented by fine appendices, including – the Clan MacGregor; Notes on Rob Roy; Scott's Lady of the Lake; and a Botanical Survey of Din Dhu Oak Wood. Expensive, but innovative, well done, and though some readers may be familiar with much of it, it is rewarding and enjoyable.

Bridge of Allan in Old Postcards: a story in pictures 1895-1945. J. Malcolm Allan. Stirling Library Services. 66pp. ISBN 1-870542-34-7. £3.50.

Some 100 cards here selected from a collection of 450, are of good quality; some have their sender's annotations, some are familiar scenes many not, and all with the author's knowledgeable and interesting notes and quotes. The inside covers start with a proposal and unrealised development plan of spa days of 1851, and end with a current plan.

L.C.

SCOTLAND'S LIBERATOR:
THE LIFE AND LEGACY OF WILLIAM WALLACE 1297-1997

Elspeth King

The celebrations for the anniversary of the Battle of Stirling Bridge, led by the Stirling Initiative Partners as part of the long term tourism strategy for the town and funded through the European Regional Development Fund (ERDF), gave the Smith Art Gallery and Museum a great opportunity to mount a popular exhibition to attract tourists and locals alike. The exhibition, *Scotland's Liberator* took three years to plan and realise. It has delivered visitors to the Smith in significant numbers for the first time since the building opened in 1874, completely overturning local prejudice that the Smith is "away from the centre of things" and "too far out of town for people to take the trouble to find it".

The exhibition has put the Smith on the visitor map of Stirling, and in its correct location – just beneath the Castle in the former royal hunting ground or King's Park, a short walk from the Stirling Highland Hotel and the Albert Hall, and in good place from which to explore the rest of the town. The visitor surveys conducted and correspondence received indicate a high percentage of satisfaction with the exhibition itself, and the curatorial rewards, in the form of additional material and information from visitors, have been good. The commercial sponsors, Maclays Thistle Brewery of Alloa, who have marketed the exhibition along with their William Wallace Ale, have been delighted with the year-long promotion. The programme of talks, concerts, plays and performances, managed by the Friends of the Smith, which has accompanied the exhibition, has been well attended and profitable. In short, this exhibition has proved the Smith to be a viable visitor attraction which, given good programming, adequate marketing and financial support, can operate as well as any other in Stirling and Scotland.

The purpose of this article is to describe how and why the exhibition and its programme was presented, what it signifies in terms of the story of William Wallace, and discuss how its success can be taken forward. The world-wide success of Randall Wallace's novel Braveheart and the Hollywood film of that name could not have provided a better starting point for an exhibition on William Wallace. Nevertheless, the task in hand was daunting, given that the Smith had only three small objects of direct relevance - the seal of the Burgh of Stirling, a medal struck for the foundation of the National Wallace Monument in 1861, and a small mid-19th century jug with a crude portrait of Wallace and the legend '*Scots wha hae wi' Wallace bled*'. The main exhibition gallery in the Smith measures 97 x 40 feet, and priority was given to locating relevant exhibits.

At an early stage, we decided to cover the legacy of William Wallace over the last 700 years, looking at what his example has signified in the centuries since his death. Most biographies or histories of William Wallace end with his death in 1305, or with a brief mention of Bruce and Bannockburn. A notable exception is Peter Reese's *Wallace* (Canongate, 1996). As the Wallace story has dominated the landscape of Stirling, occupied the minds and coloured the thoughts of its people, and has given powerful assistance to its tourism strategy for over a hundred years, we considered that story as worthy of examination.

One of the great strengths of the Smith is its own collection, most of which has been in store for the past thirty years. Although there were only three small objects directly pertaining to the Wallace story, we looked at other items which legitimately could be used in the exhibition. The material from the 1865 Cambuskenneth Abbey excavation is very important, but not visually exciting. There are shards of painted glass and original leadwork from the Abbey windows, masons' tools, and other fragments. The Trustees of Dunblane Cathedral Museum generously loaned the carved keystone which some of our tools may have been cut, and we were able to borrow from the National Museums of Scotland collection the decorated metal strongbox, pot, and gold ring from Cambuskenneth. Cambuskenneth was dedicated to the Blessed Virgin Mary, who according to Blind Harry, was a special protector of Wallace, and gave him victory at Stirling Bridge:

> Apon the morn to Stirling passit rycht
> Assumpcion day off Marye fell this cas
> Ay lowyt be our lady off hir grace!
> Convoyar offt scho was to gud Wallace
> And helpyt him in mony syndry place.[1]

With so little to illustrate the life of Cambuskenneth Abbey, we took the opportunity to commission a small stained glass panel, adapting the image from the Abbey seal, illustrating Our Lady of Cambuskenneth. This was designed and executed by stained glass artist Yvonne Smith of Glasgow. Thanks to the ERDF funding, we were also able to commission a scale model of Cambuskenneth, as well as a model of the Battle of Stirling Bridge.

The very graphic description which Blind Harry gives of how Wallace purchased the clothing, cart and stock of a potter, and went in disguise to spy out the English camp before the Battle of Biggar, gave us the opportunity of using some of our exceptional collection of green glazed medieval pottery. Wallace, unused to steering the cart, kept dropping and breaking his wares, much to the amusement of the potter and the English soldiers.[2] The story suited the purposes of our collection, much of which is broken and in shard form. Academic historians, who have been quick to dismiss Harry's account of the "so-called Battle of Biggar" and to point out how the same tales are told of Robin Hood and Hereward the Wake, have missed the value of this episode, which constitutes the earliest detailed description of a Scottish potter, dressed in threadbare gray '*gown and hois in clay that claggit was*'. The poem confirms for the first time what archaeologists have long since suspected: that earthenware pots did not travel well and were made in each locality.

In scripting the text for the exhibition, we decided at an early stage to use the extant, Scottish, pro-Wallace sources in dealing with his life and death. The academic histories which deal with Wallace favour overwhelmingly the English sources, and the chronicles of Walter of Guisborough, Matthew of Westminster, Peter of Langtoft, Lanercost, Scalachronica, and William Rishanger are quoted repeatedly at the expense of Scottish sources. This is not the place to discuss *la trahison des clercs* and the academic politics which underpin the slaveheart mentality which inhibits historians from treating Scottish sources seriously. Suffice to say that in order to avoid the usual 'balanced picture' which more often signifies a balance in favour of the English viewpoint, we elected to use the *Scotichronicon* of Walter Bower (1385-1449) the *Original Chronicle* of Andrew Wyntoun, and the *Acts and Deeds of Sir William Wallace* by Blind Harry (?1440-c1492). The first two were written by Augustinian clerics around the same time, one in Latin and the other in rhyming Scots and both contain the diplomatic arguments of the War of Independence.

The most neglected of all the texts is Blind Harry's *Wallace*, and while he clearly had knowledge of the work of Bower and Wyntoun, he claimed to base his work on a biography of Wallace, commissioned shortly after the hero's death by Bishop William Sinclair of Dunkeld from Wallace's own chaplain and boyhood friend, John Blair. Sinclair's stated intention was to send it to the Pope to appraise him of the situation. Possibly it was in part a hagiography of Wallace, to demonstrate the right of Scotland's cause and prepare the ground for a canonisation process. We shall never know until the book is found, and it is judged by many historians not to have existed.

While it is impossible to deny the existence of Blind Harry, the content of his epic history is mostly dismissed as elaborate literary fiction. The internal evidence of the text suggests that Harry was collecting and collating the traditional stories of Wallace from different parts of the country, and performing them, either through declamation or song, for a live audience. The most skilled contemporary interpreter of Blind Harry's work is Paraig MacNeil of Dunblane, and the method by which he performs it is akin to that of the storytellers in the cafés of Alexandria, Egypt, who still recount the great battles and military feats of ancient times, beating the tables with sticks at appropriate intervals, and punctuating their narrative with song.

Impartial, factual history is difficult to write at the best of times. The situation in Wallace's Scotland must have been akin to that of present day Bosnia, where, even in the 20th century, atrocities can be covered up. Some of Blind Harry's stories are indicative of these atrocities. In Book Five for example, when Wallace is being pursued by the English with the aid of a bloodhound through the wilds of Perthshire, and his companion Fawdon, whom he suspects of treachery, starts to go slow, he beheads Fawdon with a single sword blow and flees. The hound, when she finds the body of Fawdon, refuses to go further and Wallace is saved. That night, he and his men reach Gask Hall and start to prepare their food. There is a sound of horns outside. Wallace sends two men to investigate. The noise gets louder. He sends out two more. The noise increases. Finally, he goes out alone, to be confronted by Fawdon, his head under his arm.[3] The headless Fawdon pursues Wallace for his life - the kind of bloody nightmare that soldiers, from the Romans to the Vietnam veterans, have experienced. Blind Harry holds up a mirror to the reality of war, and his work is an insight into how Scots managed to survive the attempted ethnic cleansing which shaped the nation.

The text of Blind Harry's poem is not readily accessible to the general public and for that reason, the opprobrium which is usually reserved for Harry's perceived "mistakes" fell with full force on the film *Braveheart*. The novel by Randall Wallace was inspired by and scripted with the assistance of a copy of the 1722 edition of Blind Harry by Hamilton of Gilbertfield, which was de-accessioned into his possession by the University of California Library at Los Angeles.

Sculptor Alexander Stoddart, in an effort to engender new respect, admiration, and an appreciative modern audience for Blind Harry, sculpted a new, classically-inspired portrait bust of him in 1996. This was purchased for the Smith's permanent collections with the aid of the National Fund for Acquisitions, administered with government funds by the National Museums of Scotland. The bust, subtitled with a line from the poem which an English soldier uses against Wallace – *Quham thowis thou, Scot?/Who are you calling thou, you Scot?* – is directed by Harry to the present day onlooker. Who are you dismissing in such familiar terms? Scot, who are you taking for granted? The working title of the piece, 'Blind Homer, Blind Ossian, Blind Milton, BLIND HARRY', was also aimed at persuading readers to re-assess Harry's place in the epic tradition. If Harry has a fault, it is that he has no surname, and the diminutive form of his name has blinded us to his importance, both as an epic poet and as an historian.

We were fortunate that artist Owain Kirby, who works in linocut and lives in Stirling, agreed to illustrate the main label panels for the Wallace exhibition.

Blind Harry   Wallace

He undertook an impressive amount of work in a short time, illustrating the battles of Stirling Bridge, Falkirk, the incidents at Biggar, the Cambuskenneth monks, the commissioning of the life of Wallace from John Blair, Blind Harry performing the stories of Wallace, James IV preserving the sword of Wallace and the iconography of Wallace on Reform Bill banners. His soldiers, spearmen and bowmen were also applied direct to the walls by way of decoration, and he undertook the artwork which enabled us to produce large templates of the Royal Burgh of Stirling Seal for use as brass rubbings in the children's activity area.

Gallery 3 is a huge space to fill, and as a focal point for the exhibition, we had considered reconstructing part of Stirling Bridge in the gallery. The logistics and the cost of this was just too great for a temporary exhibition. We took instead the symbol for Stirling from John Harding's map, prepared for invasion purposes around 1450.[4] As on earlier maps, Scotland is shown as bisected by the Rivers Forth and Clyde, and only at Stirling – depicted as a pretty pink castle with blue turrets, and a bridge attached – is it possible to cross. The castle and bridge were realised in three-dimensional form, serving as a practical viewing platform for the rest of the exhibition. Our original intention was to clad the exhibition cases in the form of the other towns on Harding's map. In different colours they are depicted as towers, castles and little churches, rather like chess pieces ready for the taking. In this form the exhibition would also have served as a walk around Scotland, looking at different aspects of the Wallace story. Unfortunately, resources and construction time did not allow this, but the presentation was done in a limited form.

During the preparation time for the exhibition and since, we have continued to collect information on every aspect of the history of Wallace. On occasion, the information has been on our own premises; we found for example, that the Wallace triptych painted by David Scott and now owned by Paisley Museum and Art Gallery, and the great painting of the Abbot of Inchaffray blessing the troops before Bannockburn, by John Phillip, now owned by Angus Council, were both exhibited at the Smith's inaugural exhibition of 1874. Some leads are unresolved. An engraving of a drawing by Alexander Nasmyth of the Torwood Wallace Oak in 1771, was located in a book, but so far, we have been unsuccessful in finding the original, which was probably commissioned by the Eleventh Earl of Buchan (1742-1829) who had a presentation box made for George Washington from the tree. It is hoped that we will continue to add to the information on Wallace kept at the Smith, as new material comes to light.[5]

The exhibition offered the opportunity of conserving items from the collections, some of which, like the masonic stone from Kippen, reputedly the earliest in Scotland, had never been on show. The costume of the Stirling Halberdiers was cleaned and conserved, J Harrison Watson's great Battle of Bannockburn painting (1904) was conserved, the Robert Burns painting was framed, and one of the North British Furniture Manufactory model sideboards, built for the great demonstration and procession to the Wallace Monument in 1887, but broken into about thirty pieces by poor storage in the 1960s, was lovingly restored. European funding also enabled us to commission music for the exhibition from the group Aon Brach, and to issue the Smith's first CD. Other commissions included heraldic banners from Dr Patrick Barden, and a life size figure of Wallace, based on Blind Harry's detailed physical description of him.

We were fortunate enough to have Bob and Barbara McCutcheon as historical advisors to the exhibition. They worked tirelessly in setting up the exhibition, loaned their unrivalled collection of Wallace and Bruce memorabilia and publications, and invested their knowledge.

Much help came from other individuals and Friends of the Smith. The Jamieson family came as a wallpapering and floorstaining squad, while the Scotts were painters. John and Ann Scott also investigated and photographed Wallace place name sites in Dumfries and Galloway.

Requests for loans were met generously. A family who had once lived in Wallace Street, Stirling, brought in the Wallace and Bruce figures which had graced their mantelpiece there, and the story of how the family farm supplied the thatch for the roof of the National Wallace Monument when the construction was at a standstill in the 1860s. The Petrie family gave up their Wallace grandfather clock for a year. The Corrieri family donated a mug and café menu with the Wallace Monument, fittingly displayed with the Garibaldi memorabilia of the 1860s. Garibaldi, 'the Wallace of Italy', was a great supporter of the building of the National Wallace Monument. Ena Ramsay, responding to the appeal for a Wallace Monument tea cloth sold by Menzies in the 1920s, not only brought it in but joined the team of guides, set up by Peggy Roddan of the Friends, which has operated for the duration of the exhibition. Galleries throughout Scotland were equally generous with their loans, and in particular Biggar Museums, Paisley Museum and Art Gallery, Aberdeen Art Gallery and Museum, the McManus Gallery, Dundee, Perth Museum and Art Gallery, and the National Galleries and Museums of Scotland, recognised the importance of the occasion.

The Battle of Stirling Bridge offered a great opportunity of mounting a diverse, thematic exhibition of national and international interest on the subject of William Wallace. It was a theme which had never been tackled before, and brought together important objects and paintings from all over Scotland. We hope to record each item in detail, to produce a quality record for the Scottish Cultural Resources Access Network, which will provide a study resource and a 'virtual' exhibition which can be used by the public an in an educational context in years to come.

With so much local help however, in essence, Scotland's Liberator is an exhibition by and for the people of Stirling, celebrating Stirling's very important place in Scottish history. In thanks for this, I adapted the last two lines of the Scotichronicon to place over the entrance to the exhibition –

Non Scotus est Christe
cui expositio non placet iste.
(Christ! He is not a Scot who is not pleased with this exhibition.)

References

1   Harry's *Wallace*. Ed. by Matthew P. McDiarmid (Scottish Text Society Edinburgh 1968) vol 1 pp175-176.
2   ibid. p122-123.
3   ibid. p76-79.
4   British Library, Lansdowne MS 204, f.226v. See PDA Harvey *Medieval Maps* (British Library 1991) pp70-73.
5   The exhibition brochure, *The Life and Legacy of Scotland's Liberator – Introducing William Wallace*, is published by Firtree (Fort William 1997), as part of their Scottish Collection.

The Wallace Oak, Torwood – engraved from a drawing by Alexander Nasmyth, 1771.

BOOK REVIEWS

Rowing on the Forth at Stirling. The Early Years 1853 to 1906. Gordon Watson. Stirling Amateur Boating and Swimming Club. 36pp.

Scholarly interest in the history of sport, particularly that of the nineteenth and early twentieth centuries when modern forms of institutionalised and codified sport first extensively emerged, has increased greatly in recent years. As a result, our understanding of the broad nature, causes and consequences of the unprecedented transformation in Britain's sporting culture which occurred during the course of the Victorian and Edwardian periods is now reasonably well advanced. Much, however, still remains to be done not least at the local level of sporting activity and for the many sports like rowing whose appeal was both more ephemeral and less widespread than that of the major sporting recreations of the age such as football, cricket and athletics. To the extent that the present study focuses on these relatively neglected aspects of sport history it deserves a warm welcome. At the same time, the contribution it makes to the ongoing debate about the place of sport in Victorian and Edwardian society is more limited that it might have been. By adopting an essentially descriptive approach, the study pays insufficient attention to a number of issues which students of sport history would have been especially interested in. Why were patrons like MacFarlane so committed to rowing? Why did MacFarlane withdraw his support from the Stirling Boat Club? Why was the persistence of rowing at Stirling so patchy? A fuller treatment of the revived Stirling Amateur Boating and Swimming Club in the late nineteenth and early twentieth centuries would also have been instructive. Who was its patrons? What were their objectives? From which social classes did its membership come and how many members did it have? Why was rowing more successful in the later 1890s and early 1900s than at any time since 1860? Most of these questions, it is true, can only be partially answered. But, in the local newspapers alone, there is sufficient material to allow something to be said. With a more judicious balance between narrative and analysis the author's work would have been more informative. Even is it is, however, it serves as a useful reminder that more research into the development of sport at the grass-roots level is urgently needed. Hopefully, it will encourage others to follow.

N.L.T.

FROM BARBOUR TO BRAVEHEART
Re-interpreting the Battle of Stirling Bridge

Fiona Watson

This talk, in the year of the 700th anniversary of the battle, will focus primarily on the way in which this important event in the wars of independence with England has been depicted through time, and how its image as a victory for a popular army under Wallace conforms to reality. Much of this changing historiography relates to the rise of the cult of William Wallace, which will also be a dominant theme.

[This was the Dr W. H. Welsh Trust Lecture to the Bridge of Allan Local History Group on 4th March 1997.]

William Wallace will always have a special place in the hearts of the Scottish people. However, he is perhaps remembered with particular reverence by those who live in and around the Stirling area, site of the two most famous Scottish victories of all time. As an icon of pure and unadulterated Scottish patriotism, Wallace is in a league of his own and is now surely the number one Scottish hero not just in his own country, but around the world. But despite his apparent single-mindedness, he has undergone considerable transitions in his image, symbolising, for example, both nationalist and unionist within only the past century. That is the nature of a mythology – as society's prevailing ideologies change, so the hero's identity adapts to fit. However, the historical William Wallace is far less adaptable, not least because of the limits of historical knowledge about him. Unlike the myth, which has created a Wallace for all times, history shows him to be very much a man of his own time. This paper will endeavour to examine the thirteenth century Wallace within the context of the wars in which he played only a part, albeit an important one; it will then look at how he developed into the hero who apparently almost won those wars single-handedly.

Wallace's rebellion begins traditionally with the murder of the English sheriff of Lanark; he then raised the men of Clydesdale and perhaps moved south. Certainly the sheriff of Westmoreland was unable to undertake a tax assessment in that county, as he was ordered to do in a writ dated 26th April 1297, because "all the knights and free tenants are in Cumberland to defend the march between England and Scotland against the coming of the Scots". Thus, by early May, if not late April, the Scots on the western border, probably led by Wallace, were firmly in revolt. A letter from King Edward I, dated 13 June, thanking men from Dumfriesshire "for their late ready and willing service in repelling disturbers of the peace and recapturing for the king castles which had been taken by those in those parts" may indicate just how successful they were.[1]

Wallace, now joined by Sir William Douglas, moved north to Scone, where the justiciar, William of Ormesby, was holding a court. Ormesby may have been the object of particular odium, and hence the target of this attack, because, according to the chronicler, Walter of Guisborough, he "… prosecuted all those who did not wish to swear fealty to the king of England without making distinction of person". Though the justiciar escaped, word was getting around: Guisborough goes on to state that Wallace received certain messengers at Perth who arrived "in great haste on behalf of certain magnates of the kingdom of Scotland". These were almost certainly sent by the Steward, the bishop of Glasgow, and the earl of Carrick, and argues strongly for collusion between Wallace's activities and the rebellion planned by these nobles. It should be remembered that Wallace's family lands were held of the Steward.[2]

The reason for the noble rebellion, according to the surrender negotiations, was the fear of military service overseas on the part of "the middling folk" of Scotland (Edward was about to go to war with France). Fifty-seven Scottish nobles were certainly summoned to serve abroad on 24 May.[3] In addition, any Scot still imprisoned in England after Dunbar could go with Edward in return for his freedom. It was presumably also anticipated north of the border that the conscription of footsoldiers which went on in each English county with the approach of a campaign (and also, on occasions, in Ireland and Wales) would also happen in Scotland, though there is no evidence that this was Edward's intention in 1297. In reality, very few Scots actually went overseas and all who did travelled straight from English prisons.

Two of King Edward's officials, Sir Robert Clifford and Sir Henry Percy, the lieutenant in the west, entered into negotiations with Wishart, the Steward and Carrick soon thereafter and the rebellion came to an end at Irvine on 7 July 1297. However, again according to Guisborough, who had already noted collaboration at Perth, those Scottish nobles, who demanded a return to the ancient laws and customs of their land, "took so long in discussing the concessions with frivolous points, so that Wallace could gather more people to him". The ignominy of Dunbar was still too fresh in the minds of the Scottish nobility to risk an engagement with an English force and the capitulation at Irvine was doubtless regarded as the only sensible option at the time. However, their actions, deliberately or otherwise, certainly permitted Wallace and his men to make their way to Selkirk Forest in the more strongly English-held south-east, reputedly reducing several castles on the way.[4]

The murder of a sheriff, followed by the attack on Ormesby, together with the rhetoric used during the 'aristocratic' revolt, strongly suggests that there was a fierce revulsion throughout Scotland against the experience of intensive Edwardian government. It should be noted that this year witnessed the peak of opposition to Edward's regime in England itself: preparations for the war with France had unleashed all manner of deeply-resented forms of taxation, including the compulsory seizure and sale of wool. Scotland was not exempted from such treatment: both Sweetheart and Melrose Abbeys later petitioned

Edward for compensation for eight and a half and fourteen sacks of wool respectively, seized in 1297. The Scots, quite unused to this level of governmental demand, were bound to view it as highly oppressive, compounded by the fact that the regime itself was widely-regarded as foreign and illegal.[5]

The southern rebellions, perhaps partly because they took place in that part of Scotland which caused greatest concern to the English government, tend to receive the most attention. However, in terms of achievement, the most significant rebellion was arguably that of the young Andrew Murray in the north-east. It appears to have begun in late May. The first objective of Murray's force, which included the enigmatic Alexander Pilche and other burgesses of Inverness, was the castle of Urquhart, guarding the eastern end of the Great Glen. However, it is important to note that Andrew was a nephew of John Comyn of Badenoch (still in prison in England after the battle of Dunbar) and these family ties provide a potential connection with the former government of Scotland which was led by the Comyns.

Indeed Edward was so concerned about the situation in the north-east that he agreed to release both Comyn of Badenoch and his cousin, John, earl of Buchan to try to steady the area. Again it would appear that, while these men would not yet come out overtly against King Edward (they had only been beaten resoundingly in battle a year before), they did nothing to prevent Murray's activities. Certainly Buchan's excuse that Murray and his army '...took themselves into a very great stronghold of bog and wood, where no horseman could be of service...' sounds rather lame coming from a man whose family had gained an earldom by subduing the men of Moray only a few generations earlier. The treasurer, Hugh Cressingham, who seems to have had a nose for these things, certainly didn't believe it.[6] However, this waiting game also ensured that Edward himself did not direct his full attention on Scotland, since he was still presuming that the Scottish nobility were actively on his side.

With no effective support coming from the south, the fall of Urquhart and the surrounding castles, including Inverness, was really only a matter of time. Aberdeen also went over to the rebels during the summer of 1297, although the exact motivation of its sheriff, the Englishman, Sir Henry Lathum, whom Surrey accused of "making a great lord of himself", is hard to determine. It thus seems likely that, by the time they joined Wallace at Dundee around August, Andrew Murray and his men had effectively recovered control of the north-east of Scotland and re-established some form of a Scottish administration, including sheriffs, over it.[7]

Fortunately, Edward either could not, or would not, believe that the Scots posed a sufficient threat to postpone or cancel his departure abroad; while understandable, given that Scotland was not intrinsically important to him, his presence in the north would almost certainly have provided a different outcome to the year's events. Nevertheless, he certainly recognised a degree of danger and ordered measures to be taken to provide for the safety of the border. In the meantime Cressingham, at least, was taking things very seriously, going personally to Northumberland to raise troops. The muster organised for 17 July at Roxburgh produced, according to the treasurer's own letter to the king, a considerable force of 300 covered horse and 10,000 foot but its northerly progress was forestalled by the arrival at Berwick from Irvine of Sir Henry Percy and Sir Robert Clifford on the same evening. Their good news of the submission of Carrick, Wishart and the Steward, together with the assurance of hostages to be taken from key members of the revolt convinced the Scottish government – with perhaps the exception of Cressingham - that "their enemies of Scotland were dispersed and frightened from their foolish enterprise". In any case, they now had to wait for the arrival of the royal lieutenant, the earl of Surrey.[8]

Cressingham was right, of course: the situation was about to get much worse. Wallace had left the security of Selkirk Forest and was busy besieging Dundee castle when he heard word that the Treasurer had brought in a fresh army from England. Reputedly ordering the burgesses to "kepe that castell rycht stratly", he and his men set off south again. Murray was also on his way and the two forces probably met up in August, perhaps at Perth, the most obvious crossing-point of routes from Inverness and Dundee. Surrey had also finally arrived in Scotland and was firmly told on 7 September, some two weeks after Edward's departure for Flanders, to stay there to deal with the continuing unrest. However, a mere week later, he was recalled to London as civil war threatened to engulf England. This was the biggest crisis of Edward Longshank's reign and he wasn't there to deal with it.[9]

Unfortunately, Surrey, for once, was bent on action and had already gone to meet the Scots. His army, which presumably comprised those he had brought north himself and those raised by Cressingham in mid-July, was certainly not the 1000 cavalry and 50,000 foot claimed by the chronicler, Guisborough. However, it may well have been a respectable force of perhaps one-fifth of that size (200 cavalry, 10,000 foot). A similar reduction would give Murray and Wallace 36 horse and 8000 foot. Presumably most of the cavalry on the Scottish side came with Murray, the nobleman.

The exact events of the battle are either well enough known, or currently still too much in dispute, to spend much time on here, when the outcome is really what is important. However, the basic events are probably as follows, based on Walter of Guisborough's version, which itself was probably drawn from what seems to have been an eye-witness account. According to the chronicler: "And the Scots grew to enormous numbers, so that the community of the land was following him [Wallace] as leader. Even all the great families adhered to him and though the magnates had to be with our king in body, their hearts were far from him".

The English army which had left Berwick with the arrival of Surrey, marched to Stirling (which both armies had to do if they wanted to cross the Forth). There the Steward and the earl of Lennox offered to try to get the Scots to submit and promised reinforcements. However, these two then apparently got into an altercation with an English foraging party, thus riling the rest of the

English army which clamoured for revenge that night. Surrey calmed them down by saying that they would get it the next day. On the morning of 11 September, a group of about 5000 footsoldiers and more Welsh crossed the bridge and then returned. The Steward and Lennox then arrived back but with less men than they had promised. They had also completely failed to get anywhere with Wallace and Murray. Two friars then went to negotiate with the Scottish army "who were in another part of the mountains above the monastery of Scambscynel (Cambuskenneth)". Offers of peace were again refused.

This provoked a considerable difference of opinion within the English army: some hotheads wanted to avenge such insults; calmer voices demanded caution. Sir Richard Lundie, a Scottish knight, said: "If we cross the bridge we are dead. For we can only cross one by one and our enemies are on the flank and can descend upon us as they wish, all in one line. But there is a certain ford [presumably Kildean] not far from here where we can cross sixty at a time. Give me five hundred men and a moderate number of footmen and we will come upon the enemy from behind and vanquish them. Meanwhile you, lord Earl (Surrey) and the others with you, can cross the bridge in safety". This good advice was rejected but there was still severe disagreement as to whether or not they should cross. Eventually Cressingham "a pompous man and the son of death" urged Surrey to hurry up, since time is money. And so they began to traverse the bridge, a long and slow process which took much of the morning.

The Scots probably could not believe that the English were quite so stupid. The skill now lay in waiting until sufficient numbers of English knights had crossed to make it worth attacking, but not so many that the Scottish army was in any danger of defeat. In fact, most of the English army was still on the south bank. The Scots' pikemen then occupied the foot of the bridge "so that none could cross or retreat". A group of English knights under Sir Marmaduke Tweng charged at them but found themselves cut off from the main English army. They saw their men at the bridge being cut to pieces and forced their way back through the Scots to seize the bridge "by strength of arms". Of those who crossed, Guisborough says that 100 men-at-arms and 5000 footsoldiers (300 Welsh) were killed, including Cressingham, who was so hated by the Scots that he was skinned and apparently made into a swordbelt for Wallace. The Steward and the Earl of Lennox, seeing the carnage, took the opportunity to turn on the fleeing English, and relieve the baggage train of much of its cargo. Surrey remained on the south bank and when Sir Marmaduke Tweng got to him, they ordered the bridge to be broken and set on fire. Tweng was then given custody of Stirling castle and Surrey sped off back to Berwick and subsequently to London.[10]

The battle of Stirling Bridge was clearly an important milestone in the Scottish attempt to reassert independence, although, whether we like it or not, its significance was more in terms of morale, rather than any long-term military gain. It seems to be reasonably clear from chronicle evidence that Wallace played a leading role in the unfolding of the drama, although there is no reason to believe that Murray was any kind of shrinking violet. The point is, and this is brought out throughout his career, that Wallace was not intimidated by rank and most certainly had leadership qualities which stood him out and gave him authority above and beyond his own station. Certainly the death of Murray shortly after the battle meant that Wallace carried on as Guardian alone; however, there do not seem to have been any dissenting voices raised against this, suggesting that the victory at Stirling Bridge was recognised as having been the work of both commanders, not just the nobleman.

After Stirling Bridge, Wallace's main concern was to follow up his victory by clearing out as many English garrisons as possible and send a warning to England by means of raids undertaken south of the border specifically designed to terrorise the local population.[11] It cannot have failed to grab Wallace's attention that defeating Surrey in battle was one thing, but the real test, against Edward was still to come. But there is no doubt that 1297, taken on its own, was a tremendous success: the Scots had proved that they could live down the disasters of 1296 and Edward found himself more or less back to square one. For the Scottish nobility, for whom the defeat at Dunbar rendered them incapable, for the moment at least, of leading the fight against the English, Wallace, and Murray, showed that the potential for a successful fight was there, if care was taken. In that respect their role was absolutely crucial.

But we generally want to know a lot more about Wallace himself than these bare historical facts. The honest truth is that, in terms of the real historical person, there is very little else to be known and we certainly know nothing about his early life; his meteoric rise to the notice of history indicates the extraordinary times in which he lived and the extraordinary things that he himself did. However, it is understandably frustrating not to know anything about his formative years and this has inspired subsequent biographers to employ poetic licence. It is a very normal human need to understand the motivations of those whom we might seek to emulate, or, at the very least, admire.

From a historical point of view, we cannot separate William Wallace from the context in which he operated. Although he was undoubtedly a remarkable man, he did not, if we want to be particularly brutal about it, achieve all that much in his own time; although his leadership in 1297 was very inspiring, his was not the only rebellion and others were already resurrecting the Scottish cause. Wallace's active leadership of the Scottish people lasted around nine months, although that was not, of course, the end of his career. To a large extent, his importance lies not so much in what he did between 1297 and 1303, but in what happened to him subsequently. For William Wallace symbolises, quite unequivocally, the pure, undiluted patriotic sentiment which led him literally to die for his country. This, of course, contrasts with the behaviour of Scotland's more natural leaders, who all can be shown to have given in to Edward I at some time or other. While, from a pragmatic point of view, dead leaders are pretty useless, it is also the case that martyrs do marvellous things for causes.

It is as a Scottish martyr and the undiluted symbol of patriotism that Wallace has inspired writers after the wars of independence. The legend passed through a number of chroniclers writing in the century following Wallace's death: in particular, the chronicler Wyntoun, writing in Scots, kept Sir William's place in history and perhaps the additions made by later medieval writers included fragments of early ballads translated into Latin. Wallace was the people's hero and his reputation survived for the first few generations, at least, in a predominantly oral culture. This element is underlined by the fact that in the first literary work about the wars – John Barbour's Bruce – Wallace is completely written out. There is room for only two heroes in that poem - Robert Bruce himself and Sir James Douglas. Like most works of historical fiction, it knew its audience – the royal court and the descendants of both the hero king and his right-hand man.

The cult of Wallace had to wait another century and the politics of the late fifteenth century to finally take root within written culture and it was the minstrel, Blind Harry, who gathered up the mass of floating traditions to sing 'the dedis of prys and manhod'. He most certainly reflected the strong oral tradition which had taken Wallace to its heart and which, though enjoyed by the nobles before whom Hary recited his epic poem, was based on peasant culture. Harry had the authority of tradition: his contemporaries, the poets William Dunbar and John Major, regarded him as someone primarily who put together in popular verse the things commonly reported about Wallace in return for food and clothing. He was equally popular with those seeking historical fact or historical fiction. Most important, however, was the context in which The Wallace was written: this was a period in which the Scottish crown was moving towards peace with England, for the very good reason that constant friction with a stronger neighbour was not in the kingdom's best interests. However, there was a strong reaction against such a move, particularly from border society led by the king's own brother, Alexander, Duke of Albany. To this end, an epic poem with a strong nationalist, not to mention xenophobic, slant was likely to find very fertile ground indeed at all levels of society. Thus we find the immortal lines:

'Our old enemies come of Saxon's blood,
That never yet to Scotland would do good'

These sentiments made the poem a best-seller. Blind Harry's Wallace passed through more editions before 1800 than any other Scottish book; it was probably one of first issues of the printing press introduced to Scotland by Myller and Chepman around 1508. It went into a second addition sixty years later, a third edition twenty years after that and in the period after the union of the crowns (1603), it was reproduced no less than fifteen times.

Most of these editions came from the text of an Edinburgh manuscript of 1488. Three centuries later, however, the language used was regarded as profoundly old-fashioned (and rather unreadable) by most Scots. In 1722, therefore, a 'modernised version' was published in the form of a heroic couplet which captured 'the simple villages' and in 'the poor and private cottages' became a treasured classic. Once again, Wallace had gone through a transformation and instead of being the younger son of a lesser noble, he was now very much a poor but honest peasant, just like the man portrayed by Mel Gibson in the film Braveheart.

However, it was only in 1966 that a more, how shall we say, historiographical approach to the poem was published in a volume edited by Matthew McDiarmid. As a result, we finally realise just how much of the poem refers to contemporary events, that is, contemporary to Harry, not to Wallace himself. For example, reference to the 'gret kindnes' recently shown to England, of which Harry complains, is most certainly referring to King James III's unpopular policy of matrimonial alliances, inaugurated by the formal betrothal, in October 1474, of his son and heir, James, to Princess Cecily, daughter of Edward IV (this alliance did not actually come about, though it was Edward who broke it off, not James).

Equally, Wallace's fictitious campaign against the Hebridean chieftain Macfadyen, who assumes the place of the real personage of John of Lorn (who nonetheless was active in the early years of Robert Bruce's reign, after Wallace's death), is inspired by events relating to the various rebellions of John, Lord of the Isles and earl of Ross, whose submission was forced in 1476. This helps to date the poem itself, which was almost certainly written in the years 1476-8. Although there was no active English interference in Scotland at that time, as there was four years later in 1482, it is clear that Harry was reflecting the widespread and deeply held antipathy towards England, and, equally, the unpopularity of the Scottish king, whose pro-English policy certainly did not endear him to much of his nobility, nor the population at large.

There are other factors to take into account. The Scottish church, still predominantly French-educated, was still very suspicious of any rapprochement with England and its control of the education system, in the 15th century as in the 13th, was put to good use in propagating Harry's poem widely. But there was more to it than just anti-English feeling; James III was generally unpopular anyway, as a king who did not listen to his natural advisers and interfered in their affairs. He quarrelled with his more popular brothers, John, Earl of Mar, and Alexander, Duke of Albany. Harry's own sympathies are made clear in the poem, through references to two contemporary noblemen, Sir William Wallace of Craigie and Sir James Liddale – the latter in particular was closely associated with Albany. It should be remembered, therefore, that Harry's main intention was not to tell us the story of the historical figure, William Wallace, but to make a very clear plea and warning to his fellow Scots of the dangers of contemporary trends.

And he knew exactly what he was doing: as McDiarmid says, Harry knew his history in order to falsify it as successfully as he did. He claims to have followed a 'Latin buk' written by a Master John Blair, schoolfellow and comrade and chaplain to Wallace. However, it is clear that, even if such a book written by such a man existed, then Harry must have entirely ignored its contents for his assertions are so wide of the known facts. To state one obvious example, even the most mendacious of chaplains would never have suggested that his hero reached as far south as St. Albans – even the Jacobites didn't make it that far! The existence of this 'Latin buk', or at least Harry's use of it, does rather clash with the more reasonable evidence for its basis in folk tradition, a fact recognised by other contemporary poets. However, there is also clear evidence of the use of previous chronicle sources, some almost completely verbatim. Unfortunately, the surviving ballads about Wallace are all derived from the poem, rather than proving to be its source.

For Harry, Wallace is a hero and martyr of a national war, but also a holy war. He is, from an early age, devoted to the promotion of 'rychtwisnes', that is loyalty to his country and to his king, but only if the latter has the same loyalty. Despite having obvious personal reasons for rising up against the English, his motivation is nonetheless universal – it is the natural reaction of a true Scotsman faced with the invasion of his country by a brutal usurper. His death, which of course carries all the hallmarks of a romantic hero, nonetheless is shown not to have been in vain, as Scotland is now rescued by Wallace's heroic actions, and its renegade king is shamed into recognising his duty, thereby assuring Scotland's independence after Wallace's death. Though Bruce is the historical renegade king, the real target is James III.

It is not difficult, therefore, to see what Randall Wallace read before he wrote the screenplay for Braveheart. Even the incident with the Princess of Wales is in Harry, albeit in the poem the liaison is with no less than the Queen of England, wife of Edward I. And, as with Harry's Wallace, Braveheart is a popular rendition of a basic sentiment, which undoubtedly carries a resonance in our own day, reflecting a concern for 'family values'and community, as well as a more obviously modern belief that one's country is always right and fighting for one's country is always right.

So, with regard to our hero, we must recognise that there are two Wallaces with which we have been dealing. If you are interested in the historical person, who lived and died between c.1272 and 1305, then you must place him within the historical context in which he lived and assess him, his actions, and those of his contemporaries according to their own beliefs. If, however, your interest is in Wallace, the myth, the immortal hero who is now not just an inspiration within Scotland, but around the world, then Harry's Wallace and Mel Gibson's Braveheart both evoke the essence of Wallace, a black and white ability to cry freedom.

There is an important point relating to the issue of heroes and villains, which to an extent reflects badly on many Scottish historians, past and present. The recent past, historiographically speaking, has seen many revisions: kingship, for example, has been transformed by recent historians from a pitiful, beleaguered institution to a ruthless, powerful and most successful dynastic corporation, from a villain to a hero, in fact. Younger historians, in their turn, are expected to make a name for themselves by undermining that revision and thus push the pendulum back. If we play this game, then we will undoubtedly continue to miss opportunities to contribute to a wider debate and by that, I do not just mean adding an extra dimension to English history, for example.

The history of the wars between Scotland and England provides evidence for a clearly articulated sense of nationhood far earlier than is yet accepted by modern historians. But we are still not at all sure why this should be, given that medieval societies are generally community-orientated and Scotland's geography, let alone its medieval social structures, argue against the understanding of and acting upon a national issue. This subject should surely be entered into within a European, if not a global, context; but the point is that such investigations should not be regarded as attempts to solve a particularly Scottish question. This issue overlaps quite clearly with questions of mobility and communications; in particular, the degree to which certain sections of the Scottish population could and did travel abroad, or felt themselves to be part of a transnational society.

Every country needs its heroes, and, equally, its villains. But I think, without being too serious, that there is a danger, perhaps as never before, that Scottish history will become the preserve of those seeking to justify an agenda that has little to do with freedom and democracy, but more to do with prejudice and racism. We have every reason to be proud of our history, but we must leave black and white interpretations of it to the cinema. Human relations are always complex and it is only very rarely that individuals or groups are completely right and others completely wrong. To that extent, while historical icons are very useful in indicating how a nation feels about itself at any given time, they are a lot less useful in helping us come to grips with the period in which they themselves lived. By concentrating purely on William Wallace, we are in danger of ignoring not only geographical areas where he himself was not involved (not to mention all the years when he was not leading the Scottish army), but also attitudes to the war within Scotland itself which did not coincide with his own (and this does not relate only to the Scottish nobility). Finally, we must be careful to ensure that the Scottish past is not constrained by the needs of the Scottish present. Mel Gibson's William Wallace may now be known throughout the world, but he would certainly not have been recognised by his contemporaries.

References

1. M. Prestwich, *Documents Illustrating the Crisis of 1297-8 in England*, Camden Fourth Series, vol. 24 (London, 1980), p. 73; *The Cronykil of Andrew of Wyntoun*, ed. D. Laing, vol. ii (Edinburgh, 1872), p. 342; J. Bain (ed.), *Calendar of Documents relating to Scotland (CDS)* (Edinburgh, 1884), vol. ii, no. 1597; *Hary's Wallace*, ed. M.P. McDiarmid, vol. i (Scottish Text Society, 1968), pp. 34, 39; *CDS*, ii, no. 894.
2. *The Chronicle of Walter of Guisborough*, ed. H. Rothwell, Camden Society, lxxix (London, 1957), pp. 294, 295-6; J. Stevenson (ed.), *Documents Illustrative of the History of Scotland*, vol. ii (Edinburgh, 1870), p. 192; W.S. Barrow, *Robert Bruce and the Community of the Realm of Scotland*, 3rd ed. (Edinburgh, 1992), pp. 81-2.
3. Stevenson, *Documents*, ii, p. 198.

4. *Guisborough*, pp. 299, 294.
5. See M. Prestwich, *Edward I* (London, 1988) pp. 414-435, for a full account of English opposition to Edward I in 1297.
6. *Guisborough*, p. 297.
7. *CDS*, ii, p. xxx; *CDS*, iv, no. 1835; Stevenson, *Documents*, ii, pp. 217-8; see Barrow, *Bruce*, p. 86.
8. Stevenson, *Documents*, pp. 201-2; 218; *CDS*, ii, nos. 1054-5; Stevenson, *Documents*, p. 221.
9. *Cronykil of Andrew of Wyntoun*, ii, pp. 343-4.
10. *Guisborough*, pp. 300-1.
11. Prestwich, *Edward I*, p. 479; Stevenson, *Documents*, ii, p. 232; *CDS*, iv., no. 1835; *Chronicon de Lanercost, 1201-1346*, ed. J. Stevenson (Maitland Club, 1839), pp. 193, 192.

REVIEWS

Reading Perthshire: a literary guide to authors and books associated with the area. 8pp. Book Trust Scotland, Edinburgh.

One of a series of literary guides, well and colourfully produced.

Ring of Words – the Trossachs. Louis Stott. Creag Darach Publications, 1997. 40pp. ISBN 1-874585-07-5. £3.95.

This is one of a series, by the Aberfoyle author/publisher/Dunblane bookseller, about the literary topography of Scotland. Earlier issues include Stirling and Clackmannan, Loch Lomond, and Argyll. Presented excellently as a gazetteer of sites, with indexes, bibliography, helpful notes, and some illustrations.

L.C.

THE ANCIENT BRIDGE OF STIRLING:
THE CONTINUING SEARCH

R. Page

A paper in the *Forth Naturalist and Historian* (Page 1994) set out the principal facts known about the Ancient Bridge, and a survey was reported that for the first time gave the accurate positions of two massive masonry piers, presumably belonging to the ancient bridge, which had been discovered in 1905. At that time the piers had been shown, in what was admittedly a rough sketch, as lying parallel to the Old Bridge and about 65 to 75 yards upstream. Our survey, reproduced in Figure 1, found that the two piers lay at a very peculiar angle of about 60 degrees to the present river current. Bridges diagonally across rivers are extremely rare, so that many people found our survey results hard to accept.

The two piers were so far apart (33 m) that a stone arched bridge of that period was out of the question. The gap seemed also to be too wide for a single span of a wooden bridge. It therefore seemed probable that an intermediate pier had been swept away – after all, that position would take the full force of the main current of the river. Supposing that there had been an intermediate pier, other piers would have existed across the river at approximately equal intervals. Stepping out across the river on the line indicated by the two surveyed piers predicts the existence of eight piers (Figure 1).

Is it a coincidence that the Old Common Seal of the Burgh of Stirling showed eight piers? The bridge depicted on the Seal has been dismissed as fictional, on the grounds that eight piers would be far too many to cross a river about 70 m wide. That would be true for a bridge at right angles to the stream, as would usually be expected. But eight piers would be required for a diagonal bridge. Is it likely that the Old Burgh Seal would show a bridge utterly different from that recognised by the townspeople, a bridge of which they were certainly inordinately proud, important enough to figure as a main feature on Matthew Paris' map of 1247, the vital link between the south and north of Scotland?

On the assumption that the hypothesis of eight piers corresponding to the Old Burgh Seal was worth investigation, the Stirling Ancient Bridge Trust was formed in 1996[1] in preparation for the celebrations of the 700th anniversary of Wallace's victory at the Battle of Stirling Bridge in 1297. The Trust appealed for funds to carry out a Sonar survey of the river bed. It was hoped that this would reveal if any more piers were concealed under the large sand bank above the Old Bridge on the town side of the river. In the meantime an excavation was carried out in March 1996 on the south bank to look for traces of an approach road or an abutment. A similar excavation had taken place in 1907, but at that time it was assumed that the bridge went across the river parallel to the Old Bridge, so digging was from 30 to 100 yards above the Old Bridge. Nothing was found. But if our hypothesis of a diagonal bridge was correct, nothing should have been found, so we were encouraged – incidentally this shows how important it is to record negative findings; luckily that excavation was reported in some detail to a meeting of the Stirling Natural History and Archaeological Society. Our excavation close to the Old Bridge revealed a number of remains of old cottages, much disturbed by recent drains, and covered by compacted layers of dumped rubble, building debris, clay, etc. But beside the confused remnants of domestic structures and associated drains was some very large masonry, the stones of which were covered with mortar. Some of these large stones had been dislodged when a drainpipe trench had been cut through by machine. This structure seemed too massive to be associated with the quite flimsy domestic remains we found nearby. Could it be something to do with a bridge abutment or a pier? We shall not be able to decide, unless we can find something similar, also in line with the known piers, on the opposite side of the river. At some time in the future we intend to excavate there.

It was not possible to raise sufficient funds to enable the British Geological Survey to carry out a Sonar survey of the river bed early in 1996 as we had hoped, and although Stirling Council and the Tourist Board came to the rescue we had to wait until the Geological Survey team and their equipment became available in September. We were able to reduce the cost very substantially from the original estimate because a boat was made available by Mr Campbell Chesterman and Global Positioning System (GPS) equipment was provided by the Environmental Science Department of the University of Stirling to track the position of the boat throughout the survey, so that the location of the features detected could be determined. For two hours around high tide on the 25th September the boat criss-crossed the river. The Sonar record showed a number of features that were difficult to interpret, which could have been rocks, piers, or other solid objects. But the main problem was a partial failure of the GPS tracking system which meant that precise positions were uncertain for most of the time. Staff of the Environmental Science Department spent many computer hours trying to refine the results, and in the end we believed that we had located one new pier, but could not be absolutely certain. It also seemed likely that a spine of rock lay across the river for part of the line of the bridge, which could be a reason for it being built at this unusual angle.

Although the results of the Sonar survey itself were inconclusive, great interest was generated by the press and TV coverage of the survey, and this helped very much in raising funds for further work.

In April 1997 Dot Kisielewski and Shirley Plant, two members of the Stirling University Sub-aqua Club, volunteered to examine the sand bank where piers were suspected, using long iron probes. This was the method used by Bailie Ronald in 1905 that discovered a pier under the sand, and again used by us in 1992 to check his findings. Conditions were difficult. Because of recent rain the flow of water down the river was such that even at the lowest tide the water was at least chest deep, and the current flow was strong. In spite of this two more piers were located under the sand. Electronic Distance Measuring (EDM) equipment supplied by the Environmental Science Department of the University and operated by Roderick Smith (University Library Staff) enabled the positions to be accurately located. One of these was precisely where a pier under the sand had been thought likely, (see Figure 2), the other confirmed the pier possibly indicated by the Sonar survey. This pier was approximately midway between two of the predicted likely positions of piers as shown in Figure 1.

There are now three known piers under the sand and one standing clear in the river bed, all in the same straight line. It seems likely that the sand bank has accumulated because the river flow is impeded by the presence of these piers. It is possible that the excavation on the river bank in March 1996 revealed traces of either an abutment, or another pier in the same straight line. We hope that excavation on the opposite bank will reveal something similar.

A preliminary under water survey of the accessible pier was made in June by a team led by Dr Colin Martin from the Institute of Maritime Studies of St Andrews University. Once again the River Forth gave us problems. The attempt on 20th and 21st of the month had to be arranged some time in advance, to take advantage of a low tide, and in the hope that the water would be clear. But heavy rain during the previous week meant that the divers had to contend with a strong current and muddy water. Visibility near the river bed was only 10 to 20 cm, making impossible a detailed survey of Pier No 1 (the one standing out of the river bed, clear of the sand bank). Nevertheless Dr Martin was able to get a rough measure of its size, which he estimated as 7 m long. The upstream edge was obscured by drifted shingle. The downstream profile was sharper, with a tumble of boulders, mainly rounded, sloping down to the grey clay of the river bed. At least some of the stones appeared to be dressed masonry, in particular one piece 0.7 m by 0.4 m was identified. Some pieces of old wood were recovered, but Dr Martin thought it unlikely that these could be structural timbers. Such timber would probably be present only under the masonry, deeply embedded in the mud of the river bed. It could be the remains of a 'brander', a sort of raft used to construct piers of bridges built in tidal waters, as explained in the previous article in *Forth Naturalist and Historian* in 1994. A small sample of timber would allow carbon-14 dating, but this would be imprecise, at best giving a date within a hundred years or so. A large sample might allow tree ring dating (dendrochronology). This can be very precise, even telling us within a few years when the bridge was built. The wood recovered by Dr Martin appeared to be snagged timber, branches or roots brought down by the current of the river and trapped among the fallen stones of the damaged pier. Examination by Dr Crone at the Edinburgh dendrochronology laboratory confirms this – the wood is apparently willow or alder, so it was almost certainly snagged tree branches or roots brought down by the current.

We hope that when Dr Martin and his team return in September conditions will be better. Underwater archaeology in the tidal waters of the Forth has proved to be extremely problematic, the main difficulties being the strong current and poor visibility, combined with the short period at low tide suitable for working. We aim at a detailed survey of the exposed pier, and possible excavation to obtain structural timber, although extrication of a suitable sample would need careful consideration. It may also be possible, if the water is clear enough, to get a video record of the pier.

We hope that eventually we shall be able to say when the Ancient Bridge of Stirling was built, either by one of the Scottish Kings, or by Osberht, King of Northumbria, in about 860, or even by Agricola!

Acknowledgements

We are extremely grateful to our sponsors, who have very generously donated funds to enable this and future work to go ahead. These are:- Historic Scotland; Stirling Council; Argyll, the Isles, Loch Lomond, Stirling and Trossachs Tourist Board; Bank of Scotland; Gordon Fraser Trust; Glasgow Archaeological Society; Society of Antiquaries of Scotland; and Mr G. Dixon.

Note

1. The Trustees are Dr E. R. Page, Secretary, Chairman of Stirling Field and Archaeological Society, Mrs Lorna Main, Treasurer, previously Central Region Archaeologist, now Stirling Council Archaeologist, Mr James Fraser, Director of Argyll, the Isles, Loch Lomond, Stirling and Trossachs Tourist Board, Professor Donald Davidson, Department of Environmental Science, University of Stirling, and James, Earl of Mar and Kellie.

Reference

PAGE, R. 1994. The Ancient Bridge of Stirling: a new survey. *Forth Naturalist and Historian, 17*, 103-110.

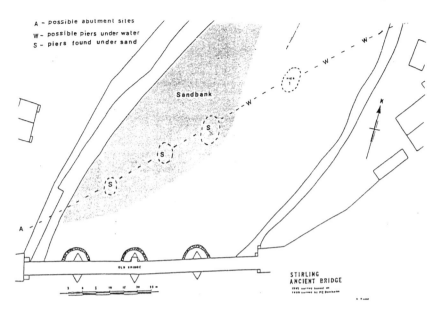

Figure 1

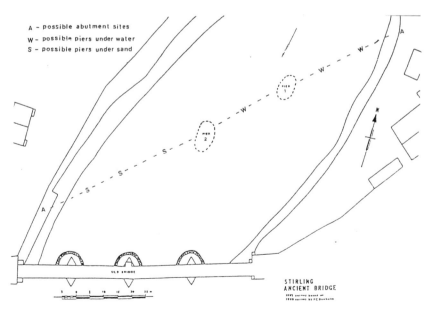

Figure 2

STIRLING OLD BRIDGE: a 16thC Reformation. A Note by John G. Harrison.

The role of Stirling's bridges in Scotland's past has often been decisive. The history of the various structures, however, is veiled in uncertainties.

Page argued convincingly that the present Old Bridge was founded in the early 15th century when building activity is attested by the Exchequer Rolls and entries in the Vatican archives.[1] Later work, it was argued, would have left further records.

The problem with an early 15th century date for the Old Bridge is that it looks like a more modern one. Stell says

The existing bridge at Stirling has wider central spans, and thus differs from first-generation multiple-arched bridges ... whose arches ... have an approximately uniform span throughout. Stirling Bridge dates from about 1500.[2]

The purpose of this note is to record a single scrap of rather unsatisfactory evidence for major work on the bridge in 1542. This was a time of national turmoil with English attacks on the Borders, the death of James V and the accession of the infant Mary. It also corresponds to a gap in the Council Record of the Royal Burgh of Stirling from 4th April 1530 to 6th December 1544.[3] Not surprisingly, an informational 'black hole' for the Stirling area.

The new information is no more than a passing mention in a volume of very miscellaneous items recorded between 1544 and 1590, the note in question, though not recorded till several years later, refers to a transaction in July 1542.[4]

At that time the Provost and Council granted to Duncan Ker the right to build a pend in the Lady Vennell of Stirling but, as usual with building work which encroached onto a public space, he was to make a payment to them. And in this case the money collected was to be 'applyit to ye help of ye Reformatioun of ye brig vork reformit be ye saids [provost and council] in ye year of God instant'.

Interpretation of this note obviously turns on the meaning of 'reformation'. In the 16th century it always seems to suggest radical change – in building as in religion. On the other hand, it is surely something less than a complete rebuilding.

Why 'reformation' was necessary remains unclear. But the chaos of the times could explain the lack of records at national level and 'reformation' in 1542 would explain the anomalous appearance of a bridge founded over a century before.

References

1. Page, R. (1994). 'The Ancient Bridge of Stirling; a New Survey', *Forth Naturalist and Historian* 17, 103-110.
2. Stell, G. (1988). By Land and Sea in Medieval and Early Modern Scotland, *Review of Scottish Culture* 4, 25-43.
3. Renwick, R. (ed.) (1887). Extracts from the Records of the Royal Burgh of Stirling. 1519-1666, p39.
4. Stirling Council Archives, B66/1/24, p149.

STIRLING BLACKFRIARS AND THE REFORMATION

R. Page and C. Page

The Blackfriars (or Dominicans, also known in France as Jacobins,) came to Stirling in 1233 at the invitation of the King. Alexander II had already installed Dominican friaries in Edinburgh and Perth. Later more were founded in other Scottish towns, including Glasgow, Aberdeen, Inverness and Ayr.

The Blackfriars were so called because they wore a black mantle over a white woollen tunic. They were not monks. Monks lived in monasteries, where their days were fully occupied with a strict time table of services and tasks to be performed within the monastery. Friars, in contrast, went out into the world to preach the gospel. They ministered to the poor and sick, acted as confessors, and collected alms. The Blackfriars were founded in 1216 in Toulouse by a Spaniard, Dominic Guzman, who had taken part in the crusade against the Albigensian heretics in the south of France. The Dominicans supported the papacy and saw their main task as the fight for orthodoxy against heresy. Indeed, in France, in the very same year that the Blackfriars came to Stirling, they were placed in charge of the Holy Inquisition, to stamp out the Cathar beliefs of the Albigensian heretics in Provence.

Like the Greyfriars, founded in 1209 by St Francis of Assisi, the Blackfriars were vowed to poverty, and were therefore not allowed to own property individually or as a fraternity. Nevertheless the accommodation provided for them, usually by the crown, was far superior to most dwellings of the time. Usually it was literally 'fit for kings', and as a result their buildings were often made available to the sovereign. For example, Edward I of England stayed 15 days with the Stirling Blackfriars while he recovered from injuries sustained at the Battle of Falkirk. James I was murdered in 1437 while lodging in the friary of the Dominicans in Perth. In Stirling, according to the Exchequer Rolls, a kitchen 'for the use of the King' was built at the friary in 1327, at the then substantial cost of 53s 4d. The luxurious life style of the Friars, contrasting with their vows of poverty, aroused some resentment, particularly among the regular clergy. They were jealous of the competition by the Friars for fees, for example for burials in their graveyards. Burial in the Blackfriars' church was prestigious. The Mammet King, the so-called Richard II of England, almost certainly an imposter, had been buried by the High Altar in 1419. The Blackfriars' church was chosen in preference to the Holy Rude church for the burial of Murdoch, Duke of Albany, after his execution in 1425. After 1475 the Pope allowed the Dominican friaries to own property, and they took full advantage of the privilege. In Stirling their properties became extensive.

Unlike the Greyfriars, whose emphasis was on simple faith, the Blackfriars' recruits were often from students of theology at the Universities. They tended to be educated and sophisticated. A typical example was Clement, head of the mission to Scotland in 1230. He so impressed Alexander II with his learning and ability that the King made him Bishop of Dunblane, the first Dominican to become a bishop in Britain. Their qualifications made Blackfriars very suitable as envoys and diplomats, and the papacy often made use of their negotiating skills. A minor example of such employment was in 1297, when the Earl of Surrey sent two Blackfriars to bargain with Wallace before the Battle of Stirling Bridge. On that occasion, of course, they failed and were sent back with his resounding refusal to surrender.

In view of their long record of orthodoxy and loyal obedience it may be surprising to find any of the Dominicans playing a leading part in the Protestant Reformation, yet several of the Stirling Blackfriars certainly did so. In 1537 Friar Killour of Stirling wrote and produced a Passion Play at the castle for King James V. This was construed as an attack on the Bishops and other prelates of the Scottish Church. Killour was seen as a dangerous heretic, and a year later in February 1538, he and Beveridge, another Dominican friar, together with the Stirling burgess, Robert Forrester, Sir Duncan Symson, a chaplain of the Church of Stirling, and Dean Thomas Forret, Vicar of Dollar, were burned at the stake in Edinburgh.

John Rough, after sixteen years with the Blackfriars of Stirling, was released from his vows in order to serve Regent Arran. Soon his views aroused the anger of the ecclesiastical authorities. He left Arran's service and after a period in Ayrshire went to St Andrews where the castle was in the hands of the Protestants. One Sunday there it was John Rough who called upon John Knox 'to take upon you the public office and charge of preaching'. This call was confirmed by the congregation. Knox recounts in his *History of the Reformation of Religion in Scotland* how 'Threat the said John, abashed, burst forth in most abundant tears and withdrew himself to his chamber'. Nevertheless he obeyed the call. After the fall of St Andrews castle, Rough spent a period in England, then went to Holland. Returning to England he was caught there by the repressions of Bloody Mary, and was burned at the stake at Smithfield in December 1557.

The Blackfriars, like other Catholic religious orders, suffered in the tumultuous events of the Reformation. In June 1559 the preaching of John Knox and others inflamed the populace of Perth to such an extent that they attacked and destroyed the monasteries and friaries there. In an attempt to control the violence, which was threatening to get completely out of hand, the Lords of the Congregation, as the reformers among the nobility were called, sent Lord James Stewart, (Earl of Moray),and the Earl of Argyle south to Stirling, Linlithgow and Edinburgh. They arrived in Stirling on the 26 June, but were too late to prevent the destruction of the friaries in the town. Knox reported 'Before their (the Lords) coming the rascal multitude had laid hands on the thieves', I should say Friars', places and utterly destroyed them'.

After the destruction of the Friary buildings the Prior, Father Andrew Makneill, granted the whole of the Dominican property in Stirling, including the Burgh Mill and the Bridge Mill, to Alexander Erskine, brother of the 6th

Earl of Mar. No doubt the Prior believed that the property would be safeguarded until better times returned. The Town Council disputed the transfer and were especially keen to obtain the two mills. The contest was too complicated to recount here, but the details are given in our forthcoming paper in the *Proceedings of the Society of Antiquaries of Scotland*.[1] Suffice it to say that after a struggle lasting 92 years the Town Council had no option but to purchase the property from its then owner, William Leslie. It never, of course, returned to the Blackfriars.

The destroyed buildings and church of the Friars lay at the foot of Friars' Street. The Friary was approximately where the Post Office and Royal Bank of Scotland stand, and the church was behind No. 64 Murray Place.[2]

Such destroyed buildings would become a useful stone quarry for other building projects. For example, the Burgh Records for 2nd November 1562, referring to St James' Chapel, also destroyed in the Reformation riots, read 'It is condescendit be the counsall that all the stanes of Saint James Chepell be brocht to the vtility and proffit of the commoun werk, and that nane thairof be disponit to ony singular persoun except thai obtene licens; and gif ony dois in the contrar to pay for tham'. It has been said that the 7th Earl of Mar built Mar's Wark in 1570-72 with stones from Cambuskenneth Abbey on the other side of the river. As James Ronald pointed out in 1890, in the *Transactions of the Stirling Natural History Society*, it would have been more convenient for him to get stones from the Blackfriars' buildings and church less than half a mile away within the town, especially as at that time his uncle, Alexander Erskine, had possession of them, even though ownership was disputed by the Burgh Council.

Thus Stirling Blackfriars played an important role in the ideological struggles leading up to the Reformation, took part in the events of the Reformation itself, and their property gave rise to a lengthy struggle during the period of readjustment of society after 1560. It is interesting to see how certain members of an organisation regarded as one of the strongest pillars of orthodoxy in religion could assist, and even give a lead, in the Protestant Reformation, as John Rough did when he proposed that John Knox should become a minister. It is also instructive to follow the progress of a society originally vowed to poverty and forbidden to own property, into a great land owner able to bequeath a problem, especially over the Town mills, plaguing the Burgh for nearly a century after their disappearance.

References

1 Page, R. & Page, C. (1997a). Blackfriars of Stirling. *Proceedings of the Society of Antiquaries of Scotland* 126, in press.
2 Page, R. & Page, C. (1997b). An excavation at the Church of the Blackfriars, Stirling. *Glasgow Archaeological Journal* 20, in press.

Addresses: Authors and Reviewers

P. J. Ashmore, Historic Scotland, Longmore House, Salisbury Place, Edinburgh, EH9 1SH.

W. R. Brackenridge, 7 The Square, Ashfield, Dunblane, FK15 0JN.

L. Corbett, Secretary FNH, University of Stirling.

D. Hall, Historic Scotland, Longmore House, Salisbury Place, Edinburgh, EH9 1SH.

J. G. Harrison, 14a Abercromby Place, Stirling, FK8 2QP.

S. J. Harrison, Environmental Science, University of Stirling.

C. J. Henty, Psychology Dept., University of Stirling.

S. Hill, Robert Gordon University, Aberdeen, AB19 1FR.

E. King, Smith Art Gallery and Museum, Stirling, FK8 2RQ.

J. Mitchell, 22 Muirpark Way, Drymen, G63 0DX.

R. and C. Page, Kingarth, Airthey Road, Stirling, FK9 5PH.

J. Proctor, DMBS, University of Stirling.

D. Spooner, 96 Halbeath Road, Dunfermline, KY12 7LR.

N. Tranter, History Dept., University of Stirling.

F. Watson, History Dept., University of Stirling.

P. Stiring-Aird, Kippenross, Dunblane, FK15 0LQ.

Forthcoming Papers

Expected for FNH vol. 21.

Built Heritage of the Forth, Flanders Moss, Community Woodlands of Dollar and Muckhart, The Wallace Oak – two papers, Jacobite Era People, Red Carr Wood.

SHELL MIDDEN AT BRAEHEAD, ALLOA

P.J. Ashmore and D. Hall

Introduction

After the last glaciation sea levels rose, and, relieved of the huge weight of ice, so did Scotland. Both of them rose at different rates at different times. Years of detailed work by Dr J.B. Sissons and others (e.g. Sissons, 1976a, 1976b; Browne, 1980) and consideration of the overall pattern of rise and fall of the British Isles and North Sea (Lambeck, 1995) has produced a detailed model of changing shore lines in the Firth of Forth. One of the particularly intriguing features of those shorelines is the presence of shell middens left by prehistoric people exploiting the shell fish of the estuary.

None of the shell middens so far dated in the Forth Valley is particularly early when compared to other hunter-gatherer sites in Scotland, for which there is now a wide range of radiocarbon dates from both the east and west proving settlement from at latest 7500 BC (Wickham Jones, 1994, p46; Ashmore, Cook and Harkness forthcoming). By that time birch and hazel had long colonised Scotland, and stands of elm and oak had started to appear (Dargie and Briggs, 1991). It seems likely that hunter-gatherers had been hunting seal and other marine mammals along the shores of Scotland, and reindeer inland, from much earlier, before birch and hazel replaced much of the tundra-like vegetation of earlier periods (Morrison and Bonsall, 1990, p134).

There are records from the Forth Valley, between Cardross in the west and Grangemouth in the east, of 15 finds of whale skeletons in the estuarine clays. They presumably represent stranded whales, and some had harpoons and other tools by them. Those west of Stirling probably belong in the period of the post-glacial maximum sea level in the Forth Valley, at some time between 5600 and 5250 BC (Sloan, 1993, fig. 3.1; Stuiver and Reimer, 1986).

The two earliest dates (so far) from an archaeological site in the Forth Valley come from a shell midden at Inveravon, West Lothian (Mackie, 1972). They are GX-2334, from charcoal in a lens of occupation material in the midden and GX--2331 for shell. GX-2334 measures 5955 +/–180 BP, which implies a calendar age of between 5280 and 4460 cal BC and GX-2331 measures 6010 +/– 180 BP which, after subtracting 405 years to allow for the differences between shell and charcoal, implies a date somewhere between 4895 and 4010 cal BC (Harkness, 1983; Stuiver and Reimer, 1986). More generally, middens accumulated from before 4500 cal BC until about 4000 cal BC. Thereafter several of the known middens were used particularly from before 3250 cal BC to after 2250 BC (to the nearest 250 years, see Ashmore, Cook and Harkness forthcoming). It may be that middens of still earlier periods remain above or below the present shoreline, for the post-glacial minimum sea level respective to the land occurred between 8000 cal BC and 7600 cal BC (Sloan 1993, 140; Stuiver and Reimer, 1986).

The Braehead midden

The site lies at NS 86939370 on the edge of Braehead Golf Course, four to five metres above the road from Cambus to Alloa, which here forms the northern boundary of frequently flooded flat fields to the north of the Forth. A stream ran southward by here at some past period and the site lies near the end of a shall dry valley where it debouches onto the flood plain of the Forth, with a low bluff to its east. The bluff tops out at perhaps nine to 10 m above the level of the road. It is covered with recent vegetation including saplings perhaps up to two or three decades old. Above it again to the east is the golf course, here built on rig and furrow with a five-metre wavelength, which ran westward down hill to the bluff. The golf club held part of the nearly land from the 1880s until the 1930s; the area was owned from Arnsbrae House. It had been grazed at least from the 30s to 1969/70, when it was given by its then owner to the golf club. There had been borrow-pitting to extract sand for sandbags in this area during the war. The appearance of the land above the site and its history seem to match each other well and may explain some of the features visible at the site.

During small-scale borrow-pitting of soil for use on the golf course, at a piece of rough ground owned by the golf club a layer of shells and thick layers of soil were exposed some 40 m north of the road. The work also exposed clay and course sand, underlying a thick layer of soil, halfway in height and distance between the road and the exposure of shells.

The local authority archaeologist, Mrs L. Main, being unavailable, and at the invitation of Mr J. Pollock, Greens Convenor, and Mr A. Finlayson, Course Manager of Braehead Golf Club, we visited on 10th September 1996 and recorded the site.

The shell exposure had previously been masked by what looked like slumped soil, a know of which remained in place with an exposure of shells to either side in a layer 0.3 to 0.4 m thick on top of fine sand. It seems possible that the soil covering the shell exposure originated in run-off from a rig system above the bluff, for it gave the impression that it had slumped in one mass from higher up, from an earlier resting point. It may be that the shells too had slumped en masse from a higher position. Certainly, that is what careful and detailed recording showed had happened in somewhat similar circumstances at the centre point of a shell midden at Nether Kinneil (Sloan, 1993).

The shell layer seemed to have been truncated on the north side of the northerly exposure and the southerly exposure seemed to have been cut through at an earlier date. There was some shell in a soil layer half way up the knob of material separating the two exposures. A bulk sample Braehead Sample 1 was collected from the upper half of the northerly exposure. It consisted largely of oyster shells (see Appendix 1). The shells did not, by and large, look well preserved. To provide a more testable reserve sample for a broad ranging date, should the shells from the exposure prove unsuitable, stray whelk and scallop shells were collected from recently disturbed loose material nearby, and bagged separately to form Braehead Sample 2. The date for Braehead Sample 1 turned out to be between 4470 cal BC and 4160 cal BC (GU-4835; see Appendix 2).

Discussion

The midden is the most northerly and westerly known in the Forth Valley (Sloan, 1993; the recent discovered Mumrills midden lies near NS 902799), and unlike most known sites Braehead lies to the north of the river. At the maximum penetration of the sea, the immediate area would have been on the south side of a large low promontory between the Forth and the Devon. If it be accepted that the post-glacial maximum sea level in the Forth Valley occurred some time between 5600 and 5250 BC (Sloan, 1993, 140; Stuiver and Reimer, 1986), the date for the midden is slightly more recent and thus it seems to have been built up during the period that the sea level was falling from its maximum extent.

D. Sloan's doctoral thesis (available for inspection in the National Monuments Record of Scotland) provides a detailed synthesis of what was known before 1993. An improved understanding of the shell middens of the Forth Valley will require a considerable amount of detailed work. However, the best current interpretation of them is that they represent just one facet of the complex life style of people exploiting a wide range of resources in the Forth Valley and its surrounding uplands (Sloan 1993, pp392-5; Wickham-Jones 1994, pp11, 69, 112).

Acknowledgements

Historic Scotland, which paid for recording the site, for the radiocarbon date and for publication.

Mr J. Pollock, Greens Convenor, and Mr A. Finlayson, Course Manager of Braehead Golf Club, for informing Historic Scotland and for allowing a record to be made.

Dr D. Sloan for access to his unpublished doctoral thesis.

References

Ashmore, P.J. (1996). Neolithic and Bronze Age Scotland. London: Batsford.

Ashmore, P.J., Cook, G. and Harkness, D.D. (forthcoming). *Radiocarbon Dates for archaeological sites in Scotland.* Edinburgh: Historic Scotland.

Bonsall, C. (ed.) (1990). *The Mesolithic in Europe: papers presented at the Third International Symposium.* Edinburgh: John Donald.

Browne, M.A.E. (1987). The physical geography and geology of the estuary and Firth of Forth, Scotland *Proceedings of the Royal Society Edinburgh* 93B, 235-244.

Dargie, T.C.D. and Briggs, D.J. (1991). State of the Scottish Environment 1991. *A report to Scottish Wildlife and Countryside Link.* Scottish Wildlife and Countryside Link.

Harkness, D.D. (1983). The extent of natural 14C deficiency in the coastal environment of the United Kingdom. In 14C and Archaeology pp351-64. Groningen August 1981.

Lambeck, K. (1995). Late Devensian and Holocene shorelines of the British Isles and North Sea from models of glacio-hydro-isostatic rebound. *Journal of the Geological Society, London* vol. 152, 437-448.

Mackie, E.W. (1972). Radiocarbon dates for two Mesolithic shell heeps and a Neolithic axe factory in Scotland. *Proceedings of the Prehistoric Society* 38, 412-416.

Morrison, A. and Bonsall, C. (1990). The Early Post-Glacial Settlement of Scotland: a Review. In Bonsall (1990) pp134-142 (see above).

Sissons, J.B. (1976a). The geomorphology of the upper Forth Valley. *Forth Naturalist and Historian* 1, 5-20.

Sissons, J. B. (1976b). The geomorphology of the British Isles: Scotland. London: Methuen.

Sloan, D. (1993). Sample Site and System: Shell Midden Economies in Scotland 6000 to 4000 BP. Dissertation submitted for the degree of Doctor of Philosophy. Cambridge University.

Stuiver, M. and Reimer, P.J. (1986). A computer program for radiocarbon age calibration. In *Radiocarbon* (ed. M. Stuiver and R. S. Kra), vol. 28 (2B), pp1022-1030.

Wickham-Jones, C.R. (1994). Scotland's First Settlers. London: Batsford.

Appendix 1: The bulk sample

Sample 1 contained the following:

Quantity	Material	Dry Weight *(g)	%of sample	Average weight (g)
113	oyster shells	1900	52	16·8
15	scallop shells	450	12	30
4	winkle shells	5	1	0·8
2	mussel shells	1	<1	0·5
–	'soil' residue (retained) with minor proportion of shattered shell	1300	35	
		3656		

*naturally dry, not kiln dried

That part of Sample 1 not used for radiocarbon dating, and Sample 2, has been deposited with Mrs L. Main of Stirling Council on behalf of Clackmannan Council.

Appendix 2: The Radiocarbon Date

A sample of scallop shells was submitted with a request to date the aragonite from the shells, rather than any calcite, because any calcite in the shell might well have crystallised from aragonite at a date well after the shellfish died, incorporating carbon contemporary with the time of crystallisation rather than with the life of the shellfish.

GU-4835 Braehead Midden, Sample 1   5880 +/–60 BP   d13C = 0·9 ppm

Calibrated age ranges (Harkness, 1983; Stuiver and Reimer, 1986)
1 sigma   cal BC 4365-4246
2 sigma   cal BC 4470-4158

There are thus 19 out of 20 chances that the calendar date for the scallop shells falls between 4470 cal BC and 4160 cal BC. Please note the convention for reporting calibrated radiocarbon dates is to use the phrase 'cal BC' to distinguish the dates (which usually have large errors attached to them) from dates obtained from historical sources or other absolute dating methods.

Shell Midden at Braehead.

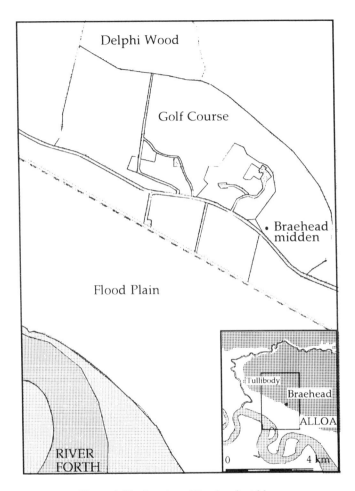

Figure 1. The location of Braehead midden.

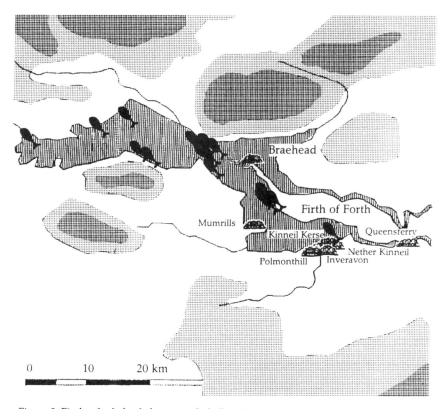

Figure 2. Finds of whale skeletons and shell middens in the upper Forth Valley, after Sloan 1993.

THE FORTH NATURALIST AND HISTORIAN

The Forth Naturalist and Historian (FNH) is an informal enterprise of Stirling University. It was set up in 1975 by several University and Central Regional Council staff to provide a focus for interests, activities and publications of environmental, heritage and historical studies for the Forth area comprising the local authority areas of Stirling, Falkirk and Clackmannshire.

The promotion of an annual environment symposium called *Man and the Landscape* has been a main feature, and 1997 is its 23rd year, with the theme Transportation – People and Environment.

The annual *The Forth Naturalist and Historian* has since 1975 published numerous papers, many being authoritative and significant in their field. They include annual reports of the weather, and of birds in the locality also some book reviews and notes. These volumes (20 as of 1997) provide a valuable successor to that basic resource *The Transactions of the Stirling Field and Archaeological Society*, 1878-1939. Five year contents/indexes are available, and selected papers are published in pamphlet form, while others eg. Ashfield Factory Village, The Weather and Bird Reports and Flora papers are available as reprints.

A major publication is the 230 page *Central Scotland – Land, Wildlife, People* 1994. A natural history and heritage survey, and exploited for schools throughout the area, also available in the form of a CD-Rom, *Heart of Scotland's Environment* (HSE).

Other FNH and associated publications still in print include – *Mines and Minerals of the Ochils, Airthrey and Bridge of Allan* – a guided walk. *The Making of Modern Stirling, Woollen Mills of the Hillfoots, The Ochil Hills* – landscape, wildlife, heritage – an introduction with walks, *Doune – historical notes. Doune in picture postcards, Alloa Tower and the Erskines of Marr*, and the *Lure of Loch Lomond*. Several of these are in association with Clackmannanshire Field Studies Society. Godfrey Maps have collaborated in producing old Ordnance Survey large scale maps of the 1890's for some 20 places in the area.

Offers of papers/notes for publication, and of presentations for symposia are ever welcome.

Honorary Secretary/Editor Lindsay Corbett,
University of Stirling, FK9 4LA, and 30 Dunmar Drive, Alloa.
Tel: 01259 215091. Fax: 01786 494994.
Web: http://www.stir.ac.uk/theuni/forthnat/